'They're just forgotten children, aren't they?'

Lorraine Johnston, Secretary in Community Child Health

forgotten children

Addressing the Health Needs of Looked After Children and Young People

The Residential Care Health Project

ISBN 0 9546292 0 5

Published by Astron
8 South Gyle Crescent Lane
Edinburgh
EH12 9EG

Contents

Foreword

Over the past decade, evidence has been gathering which highlights the dire inequalities in health care and ultimate health outcomes for children and young people whose circumstances dictate that they should become looked after and accommodated by the Local Authority because they can no longer live with their own families at home. The reasons for these inequalities are many and varied, but the clear fact is that a large proportion of these children start with neglected health in the home situation, and the window of opportunity to rectify matters when they move into the care of others has not been forthcoming. We believe that this is the fault of no one agency, more a failure of our systems to function adequately for people who do not fit into the establishment.

The residential care health project was set up therefore to look at all the factors contributing to a situation where a group of our children and young people clearly do not have access to the current health provisions which we all take for granted in our society. In so doing, we have learned so much of many lives, heard tales of great sorrow and hardship, but also of resilience, character and success. We have had very serious times with young people, but also much fun and laughter with them. We have had the pleasure of working with the most dedicated teams of people involved with caring for these young people, and have had huge support from the many agencies both mainstream and voluntary who have guided us.

Most importantly, we have seen changes – slowly at first, then gathering momentum. A system in which residential care workers were left unsupported to find their way through the health care system with little knowledge where to turn to for help has been supported to flourish and grow. We have seen children with previously unrecognised or neglected health problems seek help for them. The children and carers together are looking at health in a more holistic way in terms of lifestyle and wellbeing. Managers in the various agencies are looking at future developments to help these young people and to support their carers. The forgotten children have been found, and we owe it to them to work with colleagues in the many other agencies to help them towards the prospect of a better future both for themselves and for the generations to come.

Residential Care Health Project Team

The Residential Care Health Project team, in essence, represents one of the greatest challenges to improving the health outcomes of looked after children: that of pulling together the various professions within the many branches of the health service to work together for a population which has, to date, been excluded from any of the services set up to support children and their families.

The team brought together a wide range of expertise – paedriatrics, child development, primary care, school nursing, special needs, community education and mental health, supported by a coordinator. This enabled the development of best practice within and between the various health agencies, which could then better support those in other agencies working with children and young people.

Anne Grant paediatrician, project director
Helen MacInnes paediatrician
John Ennis general practitioner
Barbara Mahon project nurse
Lois Sinclair project nurse
Fiona Stuart project nurse
Carol Watson project nurse
Donald Morris mental health practitioner
Lucy Wiltshire coordinator

Acknowledgements

We would like to acknowledge the invaluable support we have had during the Residential Care Health Project from colleagues in health, social work, education and the voluntary agencies, without which the progress over the past years would have been impossible.

Particularly, we would like to thank Social Work management and all staff in Residential Units who have shown such commitment to improving the health prospects for the children and young people in their care.

Part 1 Getting Started

Background

During the last century dramatic improvements in the health of Scotland's population have taken place, with life expectancy increasing and premature death from major killer diseases decreasing. We remain, however, at or near the top of the 'league tables' of the major diseases of the developed world.[1] Social inequalities and lifestyle factors such as poor diet, drug and alcohol misuse, poor dental health in children and lack of exercise are now increasingly working to negate the beneficial effects of advances in medical care.[2] It is becoming clear that many of the serious health problems of adult life are related to childhood health factors,[3] and that the effects of the early abuse of children is related to health risk behaviour and disease in adult life.[4] One of the major targets set for child health providers has therefore been to look at the causes of poor health in children, and to reduce inequalities in health care.

Of particular concern has been the health of children and young people looked after by local authorities. The phrase 'looked after' was introduced in the Children (Scotland) Act 1995[5] and replaces the term 'in care', although its definition is wider than the original definitions of 'in care' and is different from the English definition.[6] A child can be looked after at home as the subject of a supervision requirement or order, or away from home either with relatives, friends, foster carers or in residential care. In Scotland in 2000 there were just over 11,000 looked after children,[7] of whom almost half were living at home. The greatest numbers of looked after children are aged 12 to 16 years, which is also the most common age range for young people living in the residential care setting.

Despite an array of statutory measures, health outcomes for looked after children are very poor. A House of Commons Health Committee report in July 1998[8] highlighted the degree of the problem. Many looked after children had undiagnosed chronic health problems, including poor and uncorrected eyesight, significant weight problems, glue ear, incomplete immunisation programmes and courses of treatment. At least one in seven young women leaving care was either pregnant or had had a baby. Mental health was highlighted as a particular problem. Mather *et al.* in 1997 highlighted the failure of health services to meet the needs of looked after children, concluding that current health systems were not very relevant to the health needs of this very disadvantaged population.[9]

Several studies have looked specifically at the mental health problems of looked after children. McCann *et al.* in 1996[10] demonstrated a prevalence rate of 67% for psychiatric disorder in young people in the care system, with a 96% prevalence for those in residential care. Chetwynd and Robb, in Glasgow in 1998, found that the carers of children in residential units rated half to two-thirds of the young people were experiencing difficulties of a severity seen in young people diagnosed with a

[1] Towards A Healthier Scotland: A White Paper on Health. Scottish Executive. 1999.

[2] Working Together for a Healthier Scotland. Scottish Executive. 1998.

[3] Lamont DW, *et al*. Early Life and Later Determinants of Adult Disease: a 50 Year Follow-up Study of the Newcastle Thousand Families Cohort. *Public Health*. 1998; 112 (2): 85-93.

[4] Felitti VJ, *et al*. Relationship of Childhood Abuse and Household Dysfunction to Many of the Leading Causes of Death in Adults: The Adverse Childhood Experiences (ACE) Study. *Am J Prev Med*. May 1998; 14 (4): 245-258.

[5] Children (Scotland) Act 1995. The Stationery Office. 1995.

[6] Plumtree A. Child Care Law: Scotland: A Summary. British Agencies for Adoption & Fostering. 1997.

[7] For Scotland's Children. The Scottish Executive. 2001.

[8] House of Commons Select Committee on Health. Children Looked After by Local Authorities. (Second report). The Stationery Office. London 1998.

[9] Mather M, *et al*. The Statutory Medical and Health Needs of Looked After Children: Time for a Radical Review? *Adoption & Fostering*. Summer 1997; 21 (2): 36-40.

[10] McCann JB, *et al*. Prevalence of Psychiatric Disorders in Young People in the Care System. *BMJ*. Dec 1996; 313: 1529-1530.

mental health disorder.[11] A study by Dimigen et al. in Glasgow in 1999[12] showed that a considerable proportion of young children have a serious psychiatric disorder at the time they enter local authority care, but are not being referred for psychological help. In Edinburgh in 1999, the Care Sick Report[13] identified that 85% of the young people in the sample studied were highly impaired socially and functionally by their difficulties, based on self-rating and carer ratings. Depression scores on the Recent Moods and Feelings Questionnaire[14] were roughly 40% higher than that of the local adolescent population and the young people made repeated reference to their feelings of insecurity and high stress levels. Young people and staff caring for them had limited information and knowledge about the nature of mental health problems, and misinformation was apparent in both groups.

In 1997 the Who Cares? Trust carried out a major consultation exercise with young people in care.[15] Many admitted to putting their health at risk in various ways, suggesting that health education messages were failing to engage looked after children. They did not feel well enough informed about growing up, body changes and sexual health, while many reported feelings of loneliness and isolation.

Saunders and Broad[16] involved young care leavers in a study to identify the met and unmet needs of young people leaving care. They found that 48% had long-term illnesses or conditions; 17% had long-term mental illnesses or disorders; 35% had deliberately self harmed since the age of 15 or 16; 60% had thought about taking their own lives; and 40% had tried to take their own life, most of whom were aged between 15 and 18.

Some initiatives have been developed around the country to address the question of the poor health outcomes of children and young people looked after and accommodated in residential care, notably in Nottingham Community NHS Trust.[17][18][19] This project stressed the need to develop a high quality, coordinated service in partnership with young people. The need for good assessment of the health and particularly the mental health status of the young people was emphasised, along with the need for staff training and delivery of health promotion and education about health-related matters.

Other developments specifically address the mental health of looked after children. In Scotland, the East Dumbarton Project[20] and the LACES project in Glasgow are targeting the mental health needs of looked after and accommodated children. In the case of the East Dumbarton project, this was aimed specifically at young people in local authority residential care.

---

[11] Chetwynd P, et al. Psychological Problems in Young People 'Accommodated' by Glasgow City Council. Greater Glasgow Primary Healthcare NHS Trust. 1999.

[12] Dimigen G, et al. Psychiatric Disorder Among Young Children at the Time of Entering Local Authority Care: Questionnaire Survey. BMJ. Sept 1999; 319: 675.

[13] Robinson P, et al. Care Sick: The Physical and Mental Health Needs of Looked After and Accommodated Children and Adolescents in Residential Care: Public Health and Inequalities. Young People's Unit, Royal Edinburgh Hospital. Scottish Executive. 1999.

[14] Angold A, et al. Development of a Short Questionnaire for Use in Epidemiological Studies of Depression in Children and Adolescents. International Journal of Methods in Psychiatric Research. Dec 1995; 5 (4): 237-249.

[15] Shaw S. Remember My Messages. The Who Cares? Trust. 1998.

[16] Saunders L, et al. The Health Needs of Young People Leaving Care. Leicester: De Montfort University, Department of Social and Community Studies. 1997.

[17] Report of the Programme Team for Health Needs of Young People in Residential Care 1992-1997. Nottingham Community Health NHS Trust. The University of Nottingham. 1998.

[18] George M. He's Leaving Home. Community Care. Jun/Jul 1997; 1178: 29-30.

[19] Polnay L, et al. Better Health for Children in Residential Care. Arch Dis Child Sep 1996; 75: 263-265.

[20] Van Beinum M, et al. Catching Children as They Fall: Mental Health Promotion in Residential Child Care in East Dunbartonshire. Scottish Journal of Residential Child Care. Aug 2002; 1 (1): 14-22.

Within Scotland, few statistics are available on the wider health profiles of children and young people who are looked after and accommodated, or on the adequacy of health service delivery to this group, but there is no reason to believe that the situation north of the border differs significantly from that in England. The Children (Scotland) Act 1995 therefore, in recognition of this, underlines the right of children who are looked after to have the same access to NHS provision and school health services as other children. It acknowledges the effects on health of early disadvantage, and recommends that care plans for children placed full time away from home should ensure adequate health care provision, including any necessary medical, psychiatric, psychological, dental or ophthalmic attention and necessary immunisations.

The problems of delivering health care to looked after children centre around the loss of 'connectedness' with family, community and school. Lynch and Gough[21] point out that in Britain primary health care services are based on registering with a general practitioner, which should provide continuity. In the government white paper Adoption: A New Approach, it is recognised that, for looked after children, frequent moves of care are the norm[22] thereby building in the potential for problems of continuity of care. This document describes how some 18% of looked after children experience three or more placements in the course of a year, an estimated 14% who become adopted have experienced six or more placements in their care history, and only 46% of children looked after continuously for more than four years have spent at least the last two years in the same care placement.

Similarly, our system of delivery of health promotion, preventive health services and screening centres around the school health service once children are of school age, so assuming that all children will attend school. It is well known that children and young people in the care system have very high rates of non attendance and exclusion, adding to the problems of a mobile population.[23]

These factors contribute to a lack of continuity of care, lack of information on past medical history, difficulties in locating records, and failure to attend appointments. In a study of residents from children's homes in 2001, Bundle[24] found a paucity of important health information in the home records. Communication between professionals involved with the health care of the children and those dealing with their social care has not been good. Carers and social workers in the past have been left unsupported to navigate their way around complex health care systems to find the basic information necessary to care for a child safely.

Children and young people living at home receive their information and guidance on health matters primarily from their parents, supplemented by the school curriculum and their peers. Looked after and accommodated children are therefore doubly disadvantaged, as they frequently come from a background of deprivation, chaos and poor parenting, often compounded by an inability to access school health promotion and health education facilities.

The Residential Care Health Project (RCHP) emerged out of the recognition that no one agency alone can remedy the situation. Social Work, Education and Health have to work closely together to deliver health care and improve the knowledge and understanding of health issues for children, young people and their carers. Health systems cannot access the young people adequately without Social Work support; social work alone cannot access the necessary health information and advice to care for children safely without support from health services; and, without improving the education of these young people, the health and social problems for their future are likely to be compounded in the cycle of deprivation.

21 Lynch MA, Gough D. Reaching All Children. *BMJ.* July 2001; 323:176-177.

22 Adoption: A New Approach. Cm 5017. Department of Health White Paper. The Stationery Office. 2000.

23 Learning with Care: The Education of Children Looked After Away from Home by Local Authorities. Scottish Executive. 2001.

24 Bundle A. Health of Teenagers in Residential Care: Comparison of Data Held by Care Staff with Data in Community Child Health Records. *Arch Dis Child.* Jan 2001; 84: 10-14.

Planning, Start-up and Development

THE POPULATION OF CHILDREN AND YOUNG PEOPLE

At the start of the project in April 2000 there were 107 children and young people in residential care in Edinburgh, 12 in East Lothian and 15 in Midlothian. This has been a constantly changing population, with a steady flow of children and young people into, out of, and around the system, resulting in the experiences gained throughout the project being based on a much larger group.

Within the City of Edinburgh at the outset of the project there were 12 local authority managed units and two units run by voluntary agencies. There were also 12 residential placements within a local authority run school for children with social, emotional and behavioural problems. Two of the units had, between them, 12 secure beds, with a turnover of approximately 40 admissions per year. East Lothian and Midlothian each had two local authority managed residential units.

Key aims and objectives

AIMS

To work in partnership with social services:

- To examine and develop the entire health care system for these young people
- To address the backlog of inadequate health provision
- To create sustainable interventions that last beyond the two-year project period
- To establish the need for input from health agencies
- To establish the need for carer support and training
- To negotiate links with other health care and health promotion agencies
- To facilitate access to primary care services
- To identify a dedicated GP service for the secure units
- To ensure that health is firmly established on the agenda in residential units

OBJECTIVES

- To provide a health care team to work in partnership with social work, to ensure that adequate health information is held at unit level on each young person to care for them safely
- To provide health input to interagency planning
- To check that preventive care is up to date
- To provide a sound comprehensive health assessment for each young person
- To assess the need for specialist services including drug and alcohol counselling, sexual health advice and sexual abuse counselling, and facilitate these service links
- To develop specific health-related training programmes for workers within residential units
- To work with other health service providers to enable them to understand the specific needs of this group of young people

Funding

1 SCOTTISH EXECUTIVE

In April 2000, funding was granted from the Scottish Executive Innovation Fund for children's services to set up the Residential Care Health Project (RCHP) to address the health care needs of children and young people looked after and accommodated by the local authority in residential care in the City of Edinburgh, East Lothian and Midlothian (the geographical area covered by Lothian University Hospitals Trust).

2 PRIMARY CARE

The application for funding for the RCHP came primarily from the Community Child Health Department of the Royal Hospital for Sick Children in Edinburgh. There was a recognition from the outset, however, that for this group of children and young people, the failures of health service delivery are distributed throughout all its facets, including community and primary care services.

To bring about sustainable improvements, it was clear that issues relating to primary care needed to be addressed, necessitating a link in at an early stage with primary care. Following discussions with the Primary Care Trust and the Scottish Executive, further joint funding was agreed to employ a general practitioner with research experience to look specifically at primary care issues in local authority residential care.

3 *HEALTHY RESPECT*

At the outset of the project, prior to the employment of staff, an initial scoping exercise mapped all health care and health promotion agencies which were working with, or planning to work with, young people in residential care. One of the main principles of the project was to work in partnership with other agencies with a view to sustainability at the end point. *Healthy Respect* is a large Scottish Executive funded demonstration project aimed at improving the sexual health of young people in Lothian and part of its remit was to address the sexual health of young people living in local authority residential care.

A service level agreement was therefore reached between *Healthy Respect* and the RCHP so that the two organisations could form a symbiotic relationship to work with staff and young people in the units, with *Healthy Respect* funding additional nursing input on RCHP. This has proved a most successful approach, combining the specialist provision of the various *Healthy Respect* partners with the in-depth understanding of the needs of the client group which the nurses have developed.

4 SOCIAL WORK

Throughout the project, we have encouraged joint funding with other agencies and funding bodies, as the focus of our work has been to encourage all agencies to view health as a joint responsibility. The social work departments involved have supported the project in funding various initiatives such as training, conferences and the writing of a health resource pack. This thinking hopefully sets a precedent for health initiatives in which all agencies have a role to play.

Advisory group

It is essential that any project working with young people in the care system has very strong interagency links underpinning it, as without mutual trust and integrated working progress cannot even begin.

An advisory group was therefore set up with the following remit:
- How best to approach and become involved with the units
- How best to approach and work with the young people
- To investigate what other agencies are doing for the children and young people
- How best to work with other agencies avoiding duplication of work
- How best to inform staff of the project
- How best to inform young people of the project
- How to access management structures in other agencies
- To be a forum for feedback from staff in units and other agencies

The advisory group comprised:
- RCHP director
- Social Work Managers and residential care managers, Edinburgh, East Lothian and Midlothian
- General practitioner
- Children's rights officer
- Senior nurse manager
- Health promotion coordinator
- Patient Services Director, Children's Services Division, Lothian University Hospitals Trust
- Child and adolescent mental health representatives
- Educational psychologist
- *Healthy Respect* representative
- Drug and alcohol education agency representative
- RCHP rotating member of staff when project started

The advisory group evolved throughout the project's lifetime, subsequently developing into a group which was able to steer the project's exit plan both up to and beyond the end of the Residential Care Health Project.

Staffing of the project
The project employed the following staff:
- 2.0 Whole Time Equivalent (WTE) nurses
- 0.5 WTE staff grade paediatrician
- 0.4 WTE GP researcher
- 0.5 WTE mental health worker
- 1.0 WTE administrative staff (reducing to 0.8 WTE)
- 0.2 WTE consultant paediatrician (project director)

Initial phase
Staff spent the first months familiarising themselves with the residential units, gaining trust, and establishing best methods of practice. Preconceived views frequently had to be completely revisited when the realities of working within the units was understood. Systems evolved according to the needs of the young people and the working practices of carers. As familiarity with the routines of the units and a respect for the expertise of those working with the young people developed, so it was possible to begin to shape practice in a manner which was acceptable to carers, young people and project workers.

Project launch

Once staff were established in their posts, an interagency launch of the RCHP was planned along with a launch of the education department's new initiatives for the education of children and young people looked after and accommodated in residential care. This was jointly funded with social work and education.

A programme was drawn up including an introduction to both health and education developments, with workshops covering access to health services, confidentiality, mental health, sexual health and personal social development.

Confidentiality

Early in the project, it became apparent that there was a potential for tension between health and social work regarding issues of confidentiality in relationship to young people who were deemed by the medical professionals to be mature enough to understand the nature and implications of their medical care.[25] Good caring in a residential care situation entails knowing as much as possible about the young people accommodated, and the sharing of information between agencies. This sharing in multidisciplinary teams is also encouraged in good medical practice, but situations did arise where there was potential for disagreement.

A short life interagency working group was therefore set up as an essential part of the early work, which developed the following statement regarding confidentiality as acceptable to both disciplines. There remain some concerns, however, among the health professionals, particularly regarding health reports, and the potential for widespread circulation without the consent or knowledge of young people. Respect for the confidential nature of health reports has been encouraged, with an acknowledgement that this information belongs to the young person and, as such, they should have ownership over access to it.

The project view is that, in future, Health and Social Work departments need to work together at a strategic level to address this issue.

Residential Care Health Project Confidentiality Statement

The Residential Care Health team is bound by consent and confidentiality guidelines as laid down by the General Medical Council, the NMC (Nursing and Midwifery Council), and the Age of Legal Capacity Act.

Modern medical practice usually involves working in teams of health care workers and, sometimes, with people outwith the health care professions, with sharing of information necessary for the care of the patient. This principle has to be respected in residential units, but young people also have a right to expect that personal information learned during a consultation will not be disclosed unless they give permission.

Exceptions to the right to confidentiality occur when there are child protection issues, or if there is a danger to the young person or to others.

Issues of confidentiality are discussed with the young people when they have contact with a member of the team. The young people are informed that health information is shared within the health team and with the young person themselves. Discussions take place regarding who else should share health information, including the reason why it would be helpful to the young person for others to be informed. If the young person refuses for this information to be shared, and there is not an issue of child protection or danger to themselves or others, it will not be possible to disclose medical information. However, it will be appropriate for the health team to talk with staff to reassure them that any health issues are being dealt with, and that no areas of concern regarding the safety of the child or of others have arisen.

---

[25] Age of Legal Capacity (Scotland) Act 1991. The Stationery Office. 1991.

Health reports belong to the young person and the health professionals. There may be occasions where there would be concerns about sharing information widely within a unit, but the young person may give permission for a named person to be informed. This should be respected where possible, with negotiation between the young person, health worker, care staff and Social Work. If the young person wishes to keep their own health record, they need to have a secure place in which to keep it.

Medical reports need to be respected as personal to the young person. If a medical report is to be discussed at a meeting, good practice is to check with the young person prior to the meeting that this is acceptable.

If aspects of confidentiality arise which are unclear, the health staff discuss this with the project manager, who will then discuss the issue with senior Social Work Management.

Team working

Around six months into the project, focused task groups were developed, each involving two or three members of the project. This evolved because of the ever increasing number of areas in which the staff saw a real need for intensive work and development. It allowed each individual to focus on a few areas, for which they were responsible, dividing the work into manageable sections. The task groups also acknowledged individual expertise within the team and remained responsible throughout for the various key areas of work, as detailed later in the report.

The areas addressed by the task groups were:
- Staff training
- Primary care strategy
- Community child health strategy
- Mental health
- Sexual health
- Dental health
- Immunisations
- Health records and tracking
- Audit and research
- Health link workers forum
- Health resource pack for carers
- RCHP news bulletin
- Development of a special interest nurses' group for looked after children

Sustainability

Concern is frequently expressed at all levels that when projects such as this end and personnel move on, much hard work is dissipated and significant long-term change is not sustained. From the outset, however, there has been a determination that any initiative started during the project must either be completed once and for all – for example in redeveloping local methods of practice – or be set up so that sustainable systems are in place to ensure continuation after the end of the project. This has been one of the greatest challenges of the project, but one which has largely been met (see Part 4: Developing Strategies for Sustainability).

In such a project, the underlying problem is *not* one of developing new services, rather of linking hard-to-reach, socially excluded young people with existing services, and of redirecting services to meet their needs. Therefore much energy and innovative thinking has gone into looking afresh at health services, and how better to access them. This has involved collaboration with colleagues in social work, education and health to analyse current patterns of delivery of health services, which tend to be quite rigid and population based, looking at opportunities for flexibility and change.

Although sustainability has been achieved for the majority of the tasks initiated, such a project is bound to expose huge areas of unmet need, the greatest of these being the need for easy access mental health and behavioural advice, and support at all levels. This is obviously a matter which cannot be addressed without additional funding, or a redirection of services in the child and adolescent mental health services. It is, however, helpful both to the Health Service and to Social Work to have a robust local picture of the issues, to assist in health service planning.

Audit and evaluation

The Residential Care Health Project has recognised the importance of research and evaluation in time limited projects such as this one. A number of studies have taken place from within the project which will fill gaps in the evidence base regarding the health of looked after children. This is essential to develop services nationally for these young people. Advocacy for this vulnerable group is made possible when one can call on pertinent research findings, and interventions are made more fundable when sound evaluation has proven their worth.

In Scotland we are fortunate to have a national body – the Scottish Institute for Residential Child Care (SIRCC), based at Strathclyde University – charged with developing research and training in the area of looked after and accommodated young people and with which the RCHP has developed important links.

Dissemination of information

LOCAL DISSEMINATION

- Information leaflets about the RCHP were developed for young people, and for carers
- A Residential Care Health Project bulletin was circulated quarterly
- Project nurses worked with the children's rights officer to include a health section in the local bulletin for young people
- Feedback exercises to Health, Social Work, Education and voluntary agencies
- Presentation to Lothian Primary Care Research Network 2002
- Presentation at NHS Lothian research day, Edinburgh 2002

WIDER DISSEMINATION

Presentations at conferences including:

- UK Public Health Association annual conference: Scottish Exhibition and Conference Centre, Glasgow 2002
- Royal Institute of Public Health: London 2002
- Presentation at Scottish Primary Care Research Symposium, Aberdeen 2002
- 'Public Health Matters' (NHS Lothian): Edinburgh International Conference Centre 2002
- Scottish Throughcare forum: Glasgow 2002
- Scottish Association of Community Child Health conference 2002
- British Agency for Adoption and Fostering annual Scottish conference 2003
- Scottish Institute for Residential Child Care annual conference 2003

PUBLICATIONS

Grant AM. Health of Socially Excluded Groups: Lessons Must Be Applied. *BMJ.* Nov 2001; 323: 1071.

Grant AM, Ennis J, Stuart F. Looking After Health: A Joint Working Approach to Improving the Health Outcomes of Looked After and Accommodated Children and Young People. *Scottish Journal of Residential Child Care.* Aug 2002; 1 (1): 23-29.

Part 2 Interventions and Findings from Needs Analyses

Introduction

The first task of the Residential Care Health Project (RCHP), was to look analytically at the core areas which, past research has suggested, are the root causes of difficulty in delivering health services to children and young people who are looked after and accommodated, and to obtain a profile of the situation locally. The areas looked at included the health status of the children and young people, the adequacy of health information held on the young people in units, access to primary care services, and staff knowledge and understanding of health issues. Any information gathered throughout the project has formed the basis for working towards sustainable interventions to improve the long-term health of the young people. The information gathered was also essential in defining the role of the various professionals within the project, particularly the evolving nurses' role.

Four needs assessments were therefore initiated to ask the following questions:

CHILDREN AND YOUNG PEOPLE
COMPREHENSIVE HEALTH ASSESSMENTS: AN OBSERVATIONAL STUDY

- What is the health profile of the group of young people in our units?
- What are the needs for health service provisions?
- What interventions are required?
- What services are used?
- What further developments are required?
- Is the current Health Service delivery working for these children and young people?

UNIT HELD HEALTH RECORDS: INITIAL AUDIT

- How much health information is held at unit level?
- What is the system for collating health information?
- With the advent of the new 'Looking After Children' materials, how much of the information deemed to be essential for the care of young people is actually held at the unit?
- How can Health Services work with Social Work to help to collate and store information securely?

PRIMARY CARE: NEEDS ANALYSIS

- What are the views of residential care staff on the primary care of looked after children?
- What are the challenges for residential care officers relating to primary care issues?
- What are the views of primary care providers on the primary care of looked after children?
- What are the challenges for primary care providers?

RESIDENTIAL CARE STAFF: AUDIT OF TRAINING NEEDS

- Do staff feel they have the knowledge and skills to work with various health difficulties or issues?
- In what areas would they most value training?
- How easy is it for staff to access health information?

These studies underpinned the entire project in terms of interventions, service development and recommendations, and also helped project staff to work alongside unit staff and social work management in the process of identifying and implementing areas of development.

Comprehensive Health Assessments (CHA)

At the start of the Residential Care Health Project in April 2000, there were 134 children and young people resident in the 17 units covered by the RCHP. This population tends to change constantly as young people move around the residential care setting. For example, some will have a spell in a secure unit and then return to the original unit, some will move to other local authority care settings, a few will return home, and some leave to move into their own tenancies or other adult provisions, while children will be admitted anew to the units. For the duration of the project, the Staff Grade Paediatrician offered a comprehensive health assessment to as many of the young people as possible, with the aim of providing a baseline measurement of health from which individual interventions could be offered. The breadth of health interventions needed by the group underpinned much of the subsequent work on the delivery of health service provision to this hard-to-reach group of young people. The health profile of the young people was audited throughout the course of the project and it provided the evidence base to negotiate with other health care providers regarding the need for improvements in service provision and delivery.

OBJECTIVES

- To assess and measure the health needs of the young people in residential units using a model of a comprehensive health assessment rather than a routine medical
- To produce comprehensive reports for interagency discussion
- To recommend and develop a health care plan for the young person, in line with the recommendations of the Children (Scotland) Act 1995
- To initiate any referrals to primary care for further treatment
- To refer to specialist services – such as mental health services, sexual health services, occupational therapy
- To liaise with primary care, social work and other agencies
- To establish immunisation status
- To develop the young person's own health awareness through discussion of the health assessment recommendations
- To encourage the promotion of a healthy lifestyle for the young person – including dental care, healthy diet and addressing risk taking behaviour (such as unsafe sex and substance misuse)
- To liaise with the young person's key worker and support them in developing the young person's health care plan

METHOD

The Staff Grade Paediatrician initially visited all units and the aims and objectives of the comprehensive health assessment were discussed with unit managers, staff and any young people present. The process of the consultation was described and staff members were encouraged to discuss the offer of a health assessment with young people in their units.

The structure of the consultation

INITIAL STAGE

A 5- to 10-minute discussion with the young person explaining:

- The role of the paediatrician in the project
- The purpose of the health assessment
- What exactly would happen
- The voluntary nature of the health assessment
- The health assessment was confidential
- The young person could end the consultation at any time

- The young person did not need to disclose anything they did not want to, however, if it involved child protection issues, the paediatrician would have to act on any such information
- A report would be generated with health care plan recommendations
- The report would be shared with themselves, their own general practitioner and other professionals involved with them – for example social worker, keyworker – with their permission

SECOND STAGE

With the young person's agreement a 40-minute consultation followed, recording their health history under these headings:

- Current health concerns
- Past medical history
- Family history
- Medication
- Allergies
- Hearing concerns
- Vision concerns
- Dental attendance
- Immunisation status
- Review of the young person's health systems
- Substance use
- Mental health assessment
- An assessment of any learning difficulties
- Discussion of their likes, wishes and dislikes

Throughout this period the paediatrician observed the young person's interaction, eye contact, speech flow and content, physical presentation and non-verbal body language. Understandably this was a valuable aid to the overall health assessment and contributed to their mental health assessment.

THIRD STAGE

Next followed a physical examination, which was completed in the presence of a same sex residential care officer of their choice. The physical examination included a measurement of height and weight. Visual acuity was measured if it had not previously been assessed.

Other assessment tools which were used as clinically indicated included:

- Recent Mood and Feelings Questionnaire (depression)[1]
- Gillberg Questionnaire (Asperger syndrome)[2]
- Conners' Rating Scale (ADHD)[3]
- Quick Neurological Screening Test (Motor coordination problems)[4]
- Griffiths Developmental Assessment Scales[5]
- Maclure Reading Scales[6]

---

[1] Angold A, et al. Development of a Short Questionnaire for Use in Epidemiological Studies of Depression in Children and Adolescents. International Journal of Methods in Psychiatric Research. Dec 1995; 5 (4): 237-249.

[2] Gillberg C, et al. The Biology of the Autistic Syndromes. Mac Keith Press. 1992. Ch 3: 44.

[3] Conners CK. Conners' Rating Scale (Rev) MHS. 1997.

[4] Mutti M, et al. Quick Neurological Screening Test (Rev) Academic Therapy Publications.1978.

[5] Griffiths R. The Abilities of Babies. ARICD. 1954. Griffiths R. The Abilities of Young Children. ARICD. 1971.

[6] Clarke C. Maclure Reading Type for Children (Maclure Test Type). HS International. Undated.

FINAL STAGE

A 10- to 15-minute discussion followed with the young person detailing findings and recommendations to their health care plan. The report and the contents of the assessment were discussed and whether the young person wanted anything edited from the final report when it went to wider circulation. The distribution to other professionals was agreed.

Consulting with young people in young people's centres: Challenges and solutions

As would be expected, various challenges arose in accessing young people for health assessments – from the units, from the young people, from the very nature of being physically examined, and from issues such as ownership of reports and confidentiality.

UNITS

There was a wide variety of responses from the various units requesting health assessment. One unit never requested a health assessment, while others enthusiastically requested assessments for every resident and for each new arrival.

This lack of requests may be accounted for by:

- Units having a well established and supported service from their primary care surgery
- Residents feeling secure in their health and health services available to them
- Unit staff not fully understanding the health needs of young people in the care system and therefore not being supportive in encouraging the young people to request a health assessment
- Senior management initially having a poor understanding of the RCHP, with lack of support

WHAT HELPED?

- Frequent communication between the units and the paediatrician
- Project nurses reinforcing the offer of health assessments through their work with both the staff and young people in units
- Word of mouth between units about the health assessments
- Curiosity
- Field social workers requesting health assessments
- Support of Social Work Management

YOUNG PEOPLE

Some young people, as expected, were reluctant to be seen or to discuss their health, however, the approach developed was successful in the majority of cases. The aim of adopting this approach was to have a health assessment which was valuable and comprehensive and which was carried out with the young person's full cooperation.

WHAT HELPED?

- If the unit felt the young person was reluctant to have a health assessment, the paediatrician initially visited the young person at their unit for 5 minutes, introducing herself and discussing the purpose and process of the health assessment as previously stated. The young person was then allowed time to consider this offer and the paediatrician followed up with a phone call to the unit, arranging a health assessment if agreed.

- Sometimes when the paediatrician arrived for the health assessment it was immediately clear that the appointed time was difficult as the unit was either in crisis or the young person was particularly distressed. The paediatrician did not proceed, reassuring the young person that this was not a problem and a new appointment time in the unit was arranged. The paediatrician used this time to discuss general issues and liaise with the unit and other young people.
- Sometimes young people found talking about their health and past difficult. If the paediatrician sensed this, she would either stop the interview or move the subject on to something rather superficial and return to the more difficult subjects later in the consultation. This constant changing of the level of the consultation helped considerably in gaining a good assessment.
- Sometimes the young person sensed the concerns of the units that they should have a health assessment and wanted to say no just for defiance. This was helped by repeated short visits to see others in the unit, putting no pressure on the young person. The result was that the majority requested a health assessment which was useful, voluntary and appreciated by the young person.

This method of approach had several advantages:

- It encouraged the young person to take control over their health, particularly as an accommodated young person may have very few things in their life they feel they can control
- It reduced time wasting and frustration on both sides
- It avoided confrontation and resentment
- It helped to gain trust and confidence between doctor and patient
- It reduced the young person's feelings of adult intrusions into their private lives
- It helped to give the young person ownership of their health
- A valuable health assessment was obtained
- It helped to make the young person curious about their health and therefore more likely to consent and to play an active part

THE EXAMINATION

As expected, due to many factors including their age, past experiences, current circumstances and lack of trust, young people frequently found the physical examination and touch unsettling. This was exhibited in a variety of ways:

- Anxious fidgeting
- Chattering
- Flitting eye contact
- Obvious discomfort at human touch
- Embarrassment at some tests for development and motor coordination which they felt made them look stupid

WHAT HELPED?

- Always acting with care and awareness of the young person's feelings
- Explaining everything
- Reassurance
- Monitoring one's own body language, speech and approach
- Keeping boundaries clear
- Inserting humour when appropriate
- Honesty

Throughout the physical examination, it was helpful to have a variety of consultation approaches and skills after judging the young person's anxiety and mood.

Health assessment reports and confidentiality

CONFIDENTIALITY

From the start of the assessments, it became apparent that there were a number of interpretations of good practice regarding the sharing of health reports, some having been copied contrary to the express wishes of the young person, and against their human right to privacy. Though acknowledged that this was done with all the best intentions – to share information for the better care of the child – it contravened the principles of medical confidentiality, and much work was needed to resolve this. Even stamping reports 'Restricted Access' was unhelpful as they then tended to be filed apart from the rest of the child's health information.

WHAT HELPED?

- A short life working group with representatives of Health and Social Work produced a confidentiality statement which was acceptable to both agencies
- A system whereby the report was printed with the statement *Do Not Copy without the Consent of the Signatory*. This was found to be successful, the report was filed appropriately and the paediatrician received direct requests for permission to copy

Allowing the young person to copy the report and distribute it themselves was also helpful. The decision to let a young person choose whether to share their report with, for example, their parents was deliberate for the following reasons:

- To encourage the young person's feeling of their own privacy rights
- To encourage and facilitate the feeling of the young person's responsibilities over their own health
- To encourage the young person to feel a sense of control over their own life

REFERRALS

Initial referrals for health assessments tended, not surprisingly, to be for young people about whom staff had particular concerns. It was decided that this was an appropriate way to start, moving on at a later stage to young people who were not in a crisis situation as the benefits of a holistic health assessment became obvious to staff.

The health assessments were always done in the young person's residential unit except for two who were seen at their mainstream school, along with their residential care officer.

This method of approach for health assessments enabled 105 young people to have a full, voluntary comprehensive health assessment. Previous studies have shown very low uptake of health assessments by looked after and accommodated young people.[7] It was found that the majority of young people seen were interested in their health, unlike previous findings.[8] Several of the young people requested further appointments with the paediatrician to discuss more sensitive health issues, which they had not discussed in the initial assessment.

---

[7] Payne H, *et al. Ambulatory Child Health*. 1998; 4: 165-172.

[8] Mather M, *et al.* The Statutory Medical and Health Needs of Looked After Children: Time for a Radical Review? *Adoption & Fostering.* Summer 1997; 21 (2): 36-40.

Accommodated young people have always found confidentiality and sharing of their information difficult[9] which may have influenced their decisions on refusing in these previous studies.[9][10] However, using this health assessment consultation model allowed the paediatrician to develop a quality of contact, rapport and trust with the young person resulting in a valuable health assessment.

A further seven health assessments were attempted but not completed due to a variety of reasons:

- One death
- Three moved out of the area before completion
- Three refusals

The majority of young people were seen on the first visit to the residential unit and the entire assessment process was completed, on average, in an hour and a half. Preparation of the report and arranging necessary interventions took a similar amount of time.

Health assessment reports

BACKGROUND INFORMATION

Once the young person was agreeable to being seen by the doctor, background health information from a variety of sources was collated prior to the assessment. This included the information from community child health records, hospital records and from primary care, if appropriate. Immunisation details were gathered along with information about any previous child protection referrals. This background search proved invaluable in tracking health care or preventive care which had been omitted due to the various factors common to looked after and accommodated young people described in Part 1 of this report.

This information, along with the findings of the health assessment, was collated and the final report of the young person's health assessment was produced and distributed.

A copy of the report would always be retained in the community child health department and sent to their own general practitioner. The young person was also offered a copy. Only with the young person's permission was the report sent to their keyworker, social worker and any other professionals involved.

Only 12% refused to share the written report with either the key worker or their field social worker but ALL the young people agreed to share the health recommendations verbally.

If the young person had agreed to share the findings of the health assessment with their key worker, it was then suggested that they discuss the report together.

This had several advantages:

- A chance to discuss the young person's health on a one-to-one basis and encourage them to take ownership of their health
- To help action the health recommendations
- To formulate and develop the young person's health care plan
- As it was a medical report, it gave the young person a further chance for to discuss and understand the contents
- A chance for the young person to question the content or findings of the health assessment

Not one of the 105 young people subsequently queried the content of the report.

---

[9] House of Commons Select Committee on Health. Children Looked After by Local Authorities. (Second report). The Stationery Office. London 1998.

[10] For Scotland's Children. The Scottish Executive. 2001.

CONFIDENTIALITY

The confidentiality of the health assessment reports was followed as per the confidentiality statement in Part 1 (see page 7).

Observational study of the health profile of children and young people in residential care

DEMOGRAPHICS

105 children and young people were seen, 58% male, 42% female.

SEX RATIO OF THE YOUNG PEOPLE

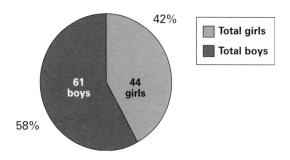

Age distribution
Age 6.3-17.8 years

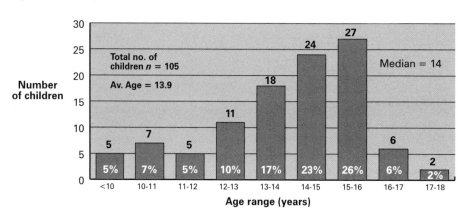

Number of schools attended

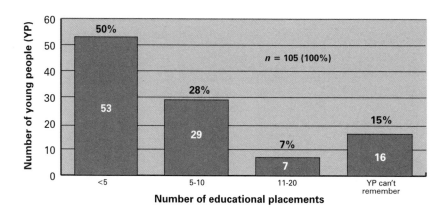

Type of educational placement

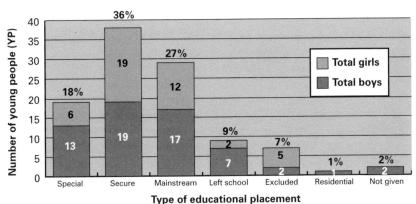

Type of educational placement

Of 105 school-aged children who were assessed:

- Only 29 (27%) were on a mainstream school roll
- Only 50% had attended less than five schools in their lifetime
- 7% had attended more than 10 schools
- 15% could not remember how many schools they had attended, suggesting multiple placements
- 7% of the young people assessed were currently excluded from school

Of the 105 young people assessed, only 13 (12%) said they knew their educational psychologist, the rest having no recollection of having been seen. Given the high levels of educational problems this is surprising.

Education is pivotal for the development of any child, but even more so for those who are accommodated away from home. A stable education can help to normalise their disrupted lives, providing 'connectedness' to their community. It reduces unstructured leisure time in their life, including the time available for risk taking behaviours or offending, enabling exposure to a wider peer group and therefore different role models. Education gives young people access to standard school health screening, preventive measures and health promotion, with access to health education programmes. It helps develop goals through academic attainments which can lead to getting out of the cycle of deprivation and disadvantage which underpins so much of the poor health of young people in the care system.

Health profile of the children and young people

Following the health assessment, any problems identified were categorised into four broad areas:

- Physical health problems
- Problems of development, learning or growth
- Missed screening or preventive care
- Emotional, behavioural and mental health problems

Health problems of young people

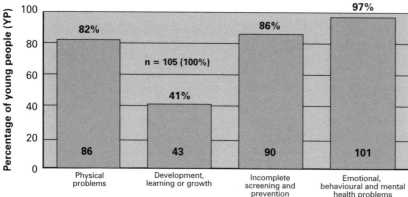

Questions were asked of the young people in areas related to their lifestyles which might affect their health and indicate the need for interventions – such as involvement in substance misuse, unsafe sexual practices – but if the young people were unwilling to answer or uncomfortable with these questions this was not pursued. The figures regarding these issues will therefore reflect those who admitted to these practices, which may be an underestimate of the need for interventions. This area was included as an important part of the clinical care aspect of the comprehensive health assessment for the individual young people, directing the need for health promotion and health educational interventions.

The physical health of the children and young people

There is well documented research that children entering the care system are at high risk of poor physical and mental health.

The early diagnosis and recognition of health problems will:

- Improve access to a variety of therapies and services
- Increase awareness and knowledge amongst the multi-disciplinary team
- Reverse any adverse influences of non treatment or recognition
- Form the basis for a health care plan

Of the 105 children and young people seen, 86 (82%) had problems with their physical health. These ranged from minor conditions which can distress youngsters – acne, warts and minor menstrual disturbances for example – to significant conditions which require to be carefully managed – including asthma, kidney problems, epilepsy or orthopaedic problems. Thirty-three (31%) of the children and young people reported having allergies.

74% of these problems were not recognised prior to the health assessment, and therefore medical assistance was not forthcoming.

It has to be remembered that many of these young people do not have the benefit of a wide choice of familiar adults with whom they can discuss sensitive personal issues, whereas young people at home can often turn to supportive parents, a GP who knows their family, a trusted guidance teacher or school nurse. It is therefore all the more important to create opportunities for young people in the care system to access accurate information regarding the management of all health conditions.

The variety of health problems encountered during the health assessments describes the wide breadth of conditions which residential care workers may encounter in their work.

PHYSICAL HEALTH AND PERCENTAGE NOT DIAGNOSED PRIOR TO ASSESSMENT

Condition	Number diagnosed	Not diagnosed prior to the health assessment (%)
Acne	13	12
Eczema/psoriasis	6	3
Athlete's foot	12	12
Miscellaneous skin conditions (for example: warts, impetigo)	13	13
Heart murmur	4	3
Renal abnormality lost to follow up	2	2
Abdominal pain, ulcer/reflux	5	3
Undescended testes	1	0
Anaemia	2	1
Thyrotoxicosis	1	0
Elevated blood pressure	1	1
Physical deformity including abnormal toes, hallux valgus, scoliosis, port wine stain, bossing, chest deformity	6	4
Dysmorphic	1	1
Cleft lip palate	1	0
Knee pain/chondromalacia patellae/ Osgood-Schlatter disease	6	6
Ingrowing toenail	3	2
Fractures	4	0
Flexion deformity – elbow	1	1
Menstrual problems including menorrhagia, premenstrual syndrome, irregularity	13	10
Vaginal discharge	13	12
ENT problems		
Perforated ear drum, otitis externa	4	3
Chronic enlarged tonsils	3	2
Neurological		
Epilepsy	3	1
Headaches/migraine	3	1
Hemiparesis	1	0
Chest condition		
Asthma	20	12

Smoking, alcohol and substance abuse

- 67% of the young people smoked and 43% smoked more than 10 cigarettes a day
- 87% admitted to alcohol use, with 13% admitting to consuming over 14 units a week
- 3% admitted to consuming over 28 units a week
- 24% admitted to solvent abuse, but all maintained this was in the past
- 61% admitted to use of other substances, the most common being cannabis (52%), but included use of cocaine, amphetamines, LSD, magic mushrooms, Methadone and valium

In 1996, Miller *et al.*[11] found that 36% of 15 and 16 year olds had smoked cigarettes in the past 30 days, 42.3% had used illicit drugs (mainly cannabis) and almost all the children had drunk alcohol. A study in Edinburgh in 1999, the Care Sick report,[12] found that 88% of the young people in residential care consulted smoked, with 48.5% smoking more than 10 cigarettes a day.

The figures confirm that smoking, alcohol and substance misuse is as much of an ongoing problem for looked after and accommodated young people in residential care as it is for young people in the rest of the community. However, for the former group it is frequently related to the high level of self-destructive behaviour and mental health problems, and has to be borne in mind as a contributing factor to some of their presenting problems.

Sexual health

Of the 105 assessed, 33 admitted to sexual activity.

Age of youngest person admitting to sex = 12.8 (girl). Age range 12.8 – 17.2.

The young people did not like being asked about their sexual activity, and it clearly brought discomfort to some. It was easier to discuss within the context of health – with the girls in particular – in relation to future fertility. Consequently, several of the girls, in particular those in the secure units, asked to see the paediatrician again to disclose concerns about a possible sexually-transmitted disease after initially denying the possibility.

Of the 33 admitting to being sexually active, 16 had unsafe sex sometimes, eight always and nine refused to answer. Not one young person said that they had always used protection when having sex.

Of the 44 girls assessed four (9%) were known to be, or to have been, pregnant:

- One was pregnant but miscarried at 22 weeks
- Two had terminations of pregnancy
- One pregnancy was ongoing

15 young people were referred for screening for sexually-transmitted diseases, of which 12 were complaining of a vaginal discharge.

These figures underline the need for special attention to be given to sexual health promotion and education for this group of young people (see Part 3, page 43 and Part 5, page 81).

---

[11] Miller PM, *et al.* Drinking, Smoking and Illicit Drug Use Among 15 and 16 year olds in the United Kingdom. *BMJ.* Aug 1996; 313: 394-397.

[12] Robinson P, *et al.* Care Sick: The Physical and Mental Health Needs of Looked After and Accommodated Children and Adolescents in Residential Care: Public Health and Inequalities. Young People's Unit, Royal Edinburgh Hospital. Scottish Executive. 1999.

Problems related to growth and development

- 43 (41%) of the children and young people were found to have growth or developmental problems
- Only 46% of these problems were recognised prior to the assessment

DEVELOPMENTAL PROBLEMS

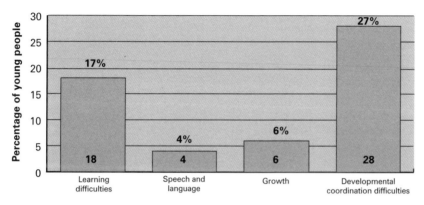

Developmental problems

PROBLEMS OF DEVELOPMENT

Issues relevant for the children and young people included developmental coordination disorder (DCD/dyspraxia: a disorder of motor coordination), speech and language problems and learning difficulties both specific and global.

For young people who are so disadvantaged socially, to have the additional burden of coping with failure brought about by a condition which could be satisfactorily managed if recognised early, is unacceptable.

There were 28 young people with Development Coordination Disorder (DCD)

- 24 were boys and four were girls
- They were aged between 6.3 and 16 years
- Six of these young people had associated learning difficulties (five boys, one girl)
- 10 were recorded as hyperactive
- Three already had a diagnosis of ADHD
- 10 of the 28 had a strong family history of drug and alcohol abuse

Young people with DCD display significant difficulties with motor skills to a level which interferes with daily life. DCD can have a major effect on the young person's self esteem and can generate a sense of inferiority. DCD may not become apparent until specific and more complex demands are made on a child in the educational setting and it may underpin early educational failure, especially where schooling has been interrupted.

Many therapies and management techniques are on offer for DCD, but the most important is *diagnosis and raising awareness*. There is a lack of knowledge generally in the population about developmental coordination disorders, and a need for those caring for children to have guidance about these matters. They should have support to identify the problems in the first place and also to access appropriate advice, treatments and materials to help the young person.

GROWTH

The height and weight of most of the children and young people was recorded, and did not differ greatly from the population mean (50th percentile).

- The average percentile for height was 44 out of a total of 88 young people who had their height recorded
- The average percentile for weight was 56 out of a total of 86 young people who had their weight recorded

Mental health

It is widely recognised that there is a high prevalence of mental health and behavioural problems in looked after and accommodated children and young people, particularly in residential units.[13][14][15] Considering the young people's life histories the high rate is not particularly surprising, as many have well recognised risk factors for developing mental health problems.[16]

These include:

- Early emotional or nutritional deprivation
- Rejection
- Maternal depression
- Family history of mental health illnesses[17]
- Family history of drug or alcohol use
- Multiple care placements[18]
- Disordered/disrupted attachments[19]
- Experience of violence within the home
- Experience of physical or sexual abuse[20]
- Loss
- Multiple separations[21]

Overall, the paediatrician felt the majority of the assessed young people were experiencing psychological distress and emotional behavioural difficulties as previously documented in the literature[22][23] and felt the level of mental health need, treatment and training was enormous. Carers identified from the outset of the project that their greatest need for support was in the area of mental health.

---

[13] McCann JB, *et al*. Prevalence of Psychiatric Disorders in Young People in the Care System. *BMJ.* Dec 1996; 313: 1529-1530.

[14] Dimigen G, *et al*. Psychiatric Disorder Among Children at Time of Entering Local Authority Care: Questionnaire Survey. *BMJ.* Sep 1999; 319: 675.

[15] Robinson P, *et al*. Care Sick: The Physical and Mental Health Needs of Looked After and Accommodated Children and Adolescents in Residential Care: Public Health and Inequalities. Young People's Unit, Royal Edinburgh Hospital. Scottish Executive. 1999.

[16] Schneiderman. Mental Health Services for Children in Out of Home Care. *Child Welfare.* 1998; LXXVII (1): 29-39.

[17] Stein E. Mental Health of Children in Foster Care: A Comparison with Community and Clinical Samples. *Canadian Journal of Psychiatry.* Aug 1996; 41 (6): 385-391.

[18] Chetwynd P, *et al*. Psychological Problems in Young People 'Accommodated' by Glasgow City Council. Greater Glasgow Primary Healthcare NHS Trust. 1999.

[19] Hamilton CE. Continuity and Discontinuity of Attachment from Infancy Through Adolescence. *Child Development.* May/June 2000; 71 (3): 690-694.

[20] Garland AF, *et al*. Types of Maltreatment as a Predictor of Mental Health Service Use for Children in Foster Care. *Child Abuse & Neglect.* Aug 1996; 20 (8): 675-688.

[21] Cantos AL, *et al*. Correlates of Therapy Referral in Foster Children. *Child Abuse & Neglect.* Oct 1996; 20 (10): 921-931.

[22] ibid. See above note 18.

[23] ibid. See above note 15.

COMPREHENSIVE HEALTH ASSESSMENTS
EMOTIONAL/BEHAVIOURAL AND MENTAL HEALTH PROBLEMS

Condition	No. diagnosed
Impaired interaction with peers	73 (70%)
Low self esteem	69 (66%)
Impaired interaction with adults	66 (63%)
Impairment of mood	30 (29%)
History of self harm	26 (25%)
Difficulties with attention & concentration	20 (19%)
Hyperactivity	20 (19%)
Anxiety	13 (12%)
Parasuicide attempt	11 (10%)
Enuresis/encopresis	7 (7%)
Obsessive/compulsive symptoms	6 (6%)
Diagnosis of ADHD	5 (5%)
Eating disorders: Obesity	3 (3%)
Eating disorders: Anorexia	2 (2%)
Eating disorders: Bulimia	1 (1%)

As can be seen by the data, the majority of young people assessed had psychological distress and emotional behavioural difficulties. However, not all required to be referred to tertiary mental health services. It was felt that there was a need for easily accessed mental health support and advice at all levels, ranging from support, training and consultation for unit staff through to the tertiary specialist level. This is further discussed in Part 3, page 43 and Part 5, page 81.

- 44 (42%) of the young people had undergone treatment in the past for mental health problems
- 20 (19%) were currently being seen at Child and Adolescent Mental Health Services (CAMHS)
- 12 (11%) were referred urgently to tertiary services by the paediatrician
- 12 (11%) were referred non urgently to tertiary services at CAMHS

Other local and community agencies which could offer support for young people and unit staff were also used, such as school-based support services, drug and alcohol counselling services, CRUSE (a bereavement support agency) and, in many cases, the young person's social worker or youth worker.

Incomplete childhood health screening and prevention

The aim of our child health service is to help all children achieve their full potential by offering a planned programme of assessment, screening and preventive services to all children. These identify, at the earliest possible time, children who may have problems, and also ensure that the population of children is fully protected against preventable infectious diseases through immunisation. The programmes start following notification shortly after birth and are a basic right of every child in the country.

Interventions start with the pre-school child health surveillance programme, then continue throughout the child's school career implemented largely by the school health programme. Areas covered include the monitoring of growth, development, dental care, vision and hearing, screening for physical health problems and ensuring that each child is immunised according to the recommended schedule.

Several studies have highlighted the poor uptake of childhood screening and surveillance in the looked after child population.[24][25][26] It was therefore important to look at these areas to assess the degree to which the children and young people in our local young people's centres had missed out on universal services, and to rectify the situation.

Four performance indicators were selected in this area.

- Incomplete immunisations
- Dental problems or those who had not seen a dentist for more than a year
- Vision problems
- Hearing concerns

INCOMPLETE SCREENING AND PREVENTION

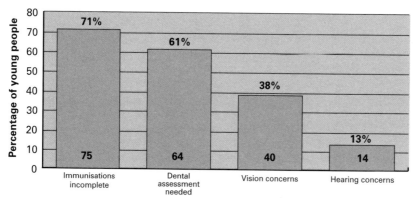

Immunisations

- 75 out of the 105 children and young people (71%) had incomplete routine immunisations

This poor uptake of basic preventive health care, which could easily be remedied, has its roots in the core problems of health care for looked after and accommodated children – coming from a background of chaos and disadvantage, multiple moves of placement, poor school attendance with inability to access school immunisation programmes and possibly the feeling that immunisations are somewhat low on the priority list for these young people, and therefore may not become part of their care plan.

---

[24] See Part 1 – Background.

[25] Hill CM, *et al.* Cross Sectional Survey of Meningococcal C Immunisation in Children Looked After by Local Authorities and Those Living at Home. *BMJ.* Feb 2003; 326: 364-365.

[26] Bundle A. Health of Teenagers in Residential Care: Comparison of Data Held by Care Staff with Data in Community Child Health Records. *Arch Dis Child.* Jan 2001; 84 (1): 10-14.

HEARING
- 14 children were referred for audiological testing due to concerns about their hearing
- For 13 of the 14 children, no one was aware that the young person was having problems prior to enquiring at the health assessment

VISION
- 40 out of the 105 were referred for a vision assessment
- 33 of these young people were not known to care staff as having difficulties with their vision prior to assessment
- Of those who had previously seen an optician (35 of the 105), 17 had not attended for over a year and only seven out of the 35 would wear their glasses

DENTAL ATTENDANCES
- 64 (61%) of the children and young people were felt, by the paediatrician, to require dental assessment, either due to dental problems or because they had not been seen for over a year

Dental health and young people in the care system is further discussed in (Part 3, page 43 and Part 5, page 81) dental health.

Health records at unit level

It is widely recognised that one of the greatest difficulties in managing the health care of looked after and accommodated children and young people is the organisation and tracking of health information. Connections are lost with family, community and school[27] with the result that health information becomes progressively less complete with each subsequent move. In order to provide effectively for the health care needs of the young people in their care, residential workers need easy access to all relevant information. The reality, however, suggests a distinct lack of continuity in the collation and transfer of essential medical details both before and between care placements.

The Scottish Executive has recently developed new 'Looking After Children' materials, to be completed by social workers for every child or young person entering the care system. These have been adopted by most of the local authorities in Scotland. In essence, these materials will ensure that the people caring for children will have as much accurate information about that child as is needed to care for them well and safely. This development embodies the concept of 'corporate parenting'; in other words, the carers should know as much about the child in their care as a good parent would, so that they can help the child to achieve as much of their potential as possible, including the best physical, developmental and emotional health outcomes.

Aware of this new development, we felt it would be valuable to establish the situation at a local level, and to assess the need for intervention. It was considered important to carry out a formal audit, based on the requirements of the 'Looking After Children' materials, which would measure the quality and comprehensiveness of young peoples' health information held at unit level. The results of the audit could be used to underpin development and change in partnership with social work colleagues. It was also an opportunity to look at the format of health records within units, and to suggest how these could be more helpful to staff and to health professionals who might become involved with the young people.

---

27 Lynch MA, *et al.* Reaching All Children. *BMJ.* July 2001; 323: 176-177.

Audit of health information held at unit level

An audit tool was designed, based on the requirements of the 'Looking After Children' (LAC) materials. Health was viewed in broad terms and reference was made to all aspects of care including identified health issues, health history, health promotion and health care planning. Over a one-month period (February-March 2001), project nurses visited each residential unit to audit files. Information about the audit was provided to staff and young people, and the purpose of the audit was discussed within units. At the request of the social work department, it was specifically the health section of the file which was audited, therefore any supplementary information that was made available could not be included in the results. Audit results were collated on the unit records of 109 children and young people. The following documents some of the main findings of the audit.

Results

WRITTEN HEALTH ASSESSMENTS WITHIN UNIT FILES

All children and young people who become looked after and accommodated by the local authority should, so far as is reasonably practicable, have a medical examination and written assessment of the state of their health and the need for health care.[28] At the start of the RCHP, practice was to document this on a locally developed 'Reception into Care' medical form, which came in two parts. Part 1 was a 'snapshot' of the child at the time of examination, and part 2 comprised more background information such as immunisation records, developmental issues and background history.

- 54% of the children had no written health assessment at all at unit level
- Of 109 children and young people, only 43 (39%) had part 1 completed, and 25 (23%) part 2

CHI (CHILD HEALTH INDEX) NUMBERS AND NHS NUMBERS

It is suggested in the LAC materials that CHI and NHS numbers should be recorded for looked after and accommodated children. It was subsequently discovered by the RCHP workers, however, that current advice states CHI numbers should not be disclosed to agencies outwith the health services for reasons of security. These numbers can enable tracking of health information from a wide range of NHS service providers.

- Of 109 records, five (4.6%) contained a CHI number and 13 (11.9%) had NHS numbers on file

GP REGISTRATION

Staff need to be clear about GP registration, and whether it is permanent or temporary.

- 44 (40%) of the notes had details of the permanent GP
- 22 (20%) had details of temporary registration
- Appointments with GPs were not routinely recorded in the health section of the files

DENTAL REGISTRATION

Regular dental checks raise awareness of the importance of diet and dental hygiene. This minimises the need for treatment and allows early detection of conditions requiring orthodontic treatment.

- 18 (17%) were recorded as registered with a dentist
- 15 (14%) were recorded as having had dental visits or treatment
- Future dental appointments were not recorded in the health section of the file. This simple measure could ensure continuity of treatment when young people move to a different unit

---

[28] Children (Scotland) Act 1995; 13 (1). The Stationery Office. 1995.

SCHOOL NURSE

- Only one young person had school nurse details recorded

IMMUNISATIONS

Immunisation is the most effective way to protect children and young people against many serious infectious diseases. There is an established timetable for giving routine immunisations from birth to teenage years, and a central immunisation record is maintained by community child health services. In order to ensure that young people in units get the same opportunity to be fully protected, it is essential that a clear record of immunisations given, due and overdue is present in the unit file.

- Only 10 (9%) had information on immunisation status

In fact, 71% of the population seen by the paediatrician had incomplete immunisations (see Part 2, page 26), so with this low level of recording, there would be no possibility of addressing this issue.

PAST MEDICAL HISTORY

The essential background information section of the 'Looking After Children' materials should contain as much detail of previous medical history as possible. This can come from many different sources including family, field social work files, and from the health services – acute, community and primary care. A comprehensive medical history should inform the health care planning within residential units. Accuracy of health information can be hard to achieve by social services alone without the full support and cooperation of health services.

- Of 109 records audited, only 13 (12%) had details of any past medical history

ALLERGIES

It is necessary that staff know of young people's allergies so that contact with allergens can be avoided and mild reactions managed appropriately. In the case of severe and life-threatening anaphylaxis, it is essential that staff are trained appropriately to deal with emergencies. From the comprehensive health assessments (see Part 2, page 20) we know that 33 (31%) of the children and young people seen had allergies.

- Nine (9%) had allergies recorded

MEDICATION

It is essential that young people are recorded as being on medication, if this is the case. Equally important is accurate recording of the dose and method of administration, especially in view of shift systems of working. This area of health care concern is highlighted in the new National Care Standards. Of the 105 young people seen by the paediatrician, 32 (30%) were on medication. This was generally reflected in the figures from the unit notes.

- 25% of young people were recorded as being on medication
- Of these, 50% had accurate recordings of the dose and method of administration

LEARNING DISABILITY

Knowing that young people have a learning disability helps staff work with them, and will effect multidisciplinary care planning. It is also important that any medical practitioner involved with the young person should be aware of learning disabilities. Of the 105 young people seen by the paediatrician in the RCHP, 18 (17%) were assessed as having a learning disability (see Part 2, page 23).

- 3% were recorded as having a learning disability

MENTAL HEALTH, EMOTIONAL AND BEHAVIOURAL PROBLEMS

It is well known that this group of young people is liable to display many features of mental and emotional distress, and ill health. It is very important that those caring for, and treating, the young people have full information about past and present concerns around mental health and emotional wellbeing. Paediatric assessment of 105 children and young people disclosed that 101 (97%) had problems in this area (Part 2, page 20).

- Of 109 young people only 13% had mention of mental health problems
- 3% had details of emotional and behavioural problems in the health files

VISION AND HEARING

Accurate recording of vision and hearing assessments improves the quality of care for young people, and also ensures that they are not being further disadvantaged in their education by impairments which can generally be easily rectified.

- 32% had a recorded vision assessment
- 14% had recorded hearing assessments

CHILD ABUSE

It is important for health care providers to be aware of past abuse and, where appropriate, it would be helpful for this to be referenced within the health section of the file.

- 15% of young people had mention of abuse within the health section of their files

DISCUSSION

The audit was carried out early in the life of the RCHP, but its true significance only became apparent after the results were compiled from the comprehensive health assessments carried out by the project paediatrician. A significant discrepancy was noted between the amount of information available to carers in the records and the true situation regarding the health status of the young people. This has proved invaluable in consultation with Social Work colleagues and health services to develop a system whereby the files contain much more, accurate health information.

A unit health record has been developed for inclusion in the unit file, which will keep all health information together in an easily accessed format. Staff are encouraged to record all health interventions – such as appointments, medication issued, health professionals involved – centrally in this record. The development of new systems for managing the health care of looked after and accommodated children (Part 4, page 73) are providing social workers and carers with the background health information required for the 'Looking After Children' materials, in a manner which was not available to them at the start of the RCHP. The carer held record, which is being issued to children and young people at the point of entry into the care system, is also held in the unit held health record for young people in residential care.

The unit health record is designed to be passed *with the young person* should they move to another unit, ensuring that vital health information is not missing on arrival. There are considerable training issues for social work staff on the management and storing of health information; health care staff have a responsibility to support and guide social work staff in this area which has previously been left to social services to manage without guidance. With good interagency working, it should be possible to develop safe and dependable ways of working so that young people attain the best possible levels of physical, emotional and developmental wellbeing.

Primary care: needs analysis

Views of residential care staff on the primary care of looked after children

BACKGROUND

There is increasing awareness that children looked after and accommodated by local authorities have greater morbidity and a poorer uptake of preventive health care than their peers. Further knowledge and understanding of the pathway to health care for looked after young people would be a step towards tackling these health issues effectively. Through experience of close interagency working, the central role of the Residential Care Officer (RCO) is recognised in this pathway and, in particular, their interaction with primary health care providers.

METHOD

We aimed to explore the views of residential care staff regarding health and their interaction with primary care services for the young people in their charge. In all, 15 residential units in Edinburgh, Midlothian and East Lothian were invited to participate in small focus group meetings between October 2001 and February 2002. Unit managers and RCOs were interviewed on site by one of two researchers, with the help of the project nurse allied to that particular unit, using a piloted semi-structured questionnaire.

The questionnaire explored three areas:

- Awareness of health problems within units
- Knowledge of sources of advice and help for health problems
- Experiences of working with primary care services

Through a process of categorisation and analysis, core themes were identified. Original data were checked against the themes and an experienced group interview analyst reviewed the process. A number of key findings drawn from this are presented here as challenges for RCOs in the context of interaction with primary care providers.

Challenges for Residential Care Officers

IDENTIFYING ILL HEALTH

- Residential Care Officers (RCOs) find it difficult to pick up on some health problems
- In particular, mental health problems are considered difficult to identify and manage longer term
- In general, residential units may have untapped resources within their own RCO teams relating to previous experience of parenthood, nursing or other health oriented training

HANDLING HEALTH INFORMATION

- Field social workers have, in the past, been the central source of information about young people for RCOs, but their reports relating to health information are currently considered inadequate
- There was wide variation in the methods of recording decisions taken at health consultations by RCOs
- In particular, full information was rarely captured for the field social worker's report
- There was a tension between the role of carer and the need to respect young people's autonomy
- In particular, RCOs need to be well informed about clinical management plans and medication for young people though they may not always be present during health consultations

Contacting health providers

- Health problems, as a whole, are often low priority compared to other pressures within residential units
- In particular, the involvement of local GPs may have been low as RCOs doubted the usefulness of the old-style reception into care medicals
- Most young people attending health appointments are accompanied by RCOs
- Some appointments are missed because RCOs are not available to cover work on the unit
- RCOs mainly contact health services in a reactive way for help with acute problems
- Currently, most health providers are not used proactively as a source of information and support about health issues in advance of an acute problem

Interaction with health providers

- Some GPs and their practice staff may not understand the work of RCOs and the predicament of looked after young people.
- In particular, while most reception staff are friendly and understanding, some are abrasive and stigmatising
- These young people find it difficult to wait in reception areas for long periods
- The new RCHP project nurses were valued as a source of advice about health issues
- Health visitors and practice nurses are recognised as an important source of information about health in general and about individual young people and families

Acknowledgement

This piece of research was carried out by Dr Ennis, Project GP, and Dr Emma Hall, GP.

Views of primary care providers on the primary care of looked after children

BACKGROUND

Access to health services in the UK is primarily through registration with a local general practitioner. Despite greater population mobility, this is often a process on a continuum from the time of birth when new parents move from antenatal to postnatal care and their new child is registered with the family general practice. Similarly, when families move into a new area, parents organise re-registration for the whole family. For children and young people looked after by the local authority, the continuum of care that exists between the family and the local general practice may be lost.

METHOD

We aimed to explore the views of primary care providers regarding health and primary care provision for looked after and accommodated young people, in particular in relation to the logistical problems encountered.

In the area covered by the RCHP, there were seven Local Health Care Co-operatives (LHCCs); each LHCC manager and medical director was contacted and a meeting was arranged with the most relevant strategic group. In attendance were the RCHP Consultant Community Paediatrician, the newly appointed nurse for looked after children and the Project General Practitioner. A brief presentation was followed by discussion on the perceived challenges. LHCC discussions took place between March and May 2002.

Subsequent to LHCC meetings and focus group meetings with residential care staff, a series of practice meetings was arranged with all 12 GP surgeries with a Young People's Centre (YPC) in their practice catchment area (three of these surgeries had two YPCs in their area). These meetings were held at a time convenient to the practice, usually at one of the regularly scheduled practice meetings and most often involving clinical staff (GPs, health visitors and practice nurses) and the practice manager. In attendance from the RCHP were the project nurse allied to the relevant YPC and the project General Practitioner. Practice meetings took place between July and September 2002.

All primary care provider meetings were minuted and additional field notes were made by the project staff. Core themes and reflections were identified and are presented here as challenges for primary care providers.

Challenges for primary care providers

GP REGISTRATION
- Patients can register temporarily if staying locally for a short time (less than three months) and fully register if joining the local community more permanently
- As looked after periods are perceived to be short, accommodated young people may not be registered permanently
- These young people may therefore never 'belong' to any one GP practice, resulting in poor relationships with staff, missed preventive care and endless 'pink sheets' (temporary casenotes)

CASENOTES AND CONTINUITY
- Casenotes are crucial in general practice to maintain continuity of care and record interventions, referrals and preventive care; they are used as a resource by all members of the primary health care team both for individual consultations and for practice-wide audit
- Casenotes are only transferred to the new GP when a patient fully registers
- Continuity of primary care often breaks down for these young people because of frequent moves between units, relatively short stays and incomplete casenotes

NEW PATIENTS AND COMPLEX HEALTH PROBLEMS
- At the time of initiating the RCHP, carers would contact a local GP for a reception into care medical for all newly accommodated young people
- GPs were left, at short notice, without notes to assess a frightened young person with no parental input whose carer had little or no background information
- The Reception Into Care medical itself served little purpose in the ongoing management of health problems for these young people
- This was therefore a dissatisfying experience for the young person, GP and carer
- This led to a view of GP health interventions as difficult, unhelpful and unwelcome

UNIT STAFF WITHOUT A HEALTH PERSPECTIVE
- Residential units are perceived to be suffering from staff recruitment and retention difficulties and are often short staffed
- Units may have fallen into the habit of calling a GP out on a house call rather than organising staff for attendance at surgery
- This is happening against the current trends for fewer GP house calls, improved GP telephone advisory services and expanding services from a wider primary care base

- Carers may not have an awareness of health issues for young people nor the range of services available and how to access them
- Reactive responses from unit staff to pressing 'immediate' health problems may mask underlying chronic health needs discouraging reflective relationships with local GP practices
- Carers may not have adequate baseline information with which to engage local GP practices in the way a parent might

Discussion

These primary care needs assessments have examined the roles and views of residential care staff, GPs and primary health care teams. Practice which enhanced good working relationships between those groups existed before the RCHP was conceived. This work has allowed these isolated elements of good practice to be shared.

In a more holistic sense, a better understanding of the challenges faced by both groups is now available to help to further develop methods and models for good practice. In particular, elements of a good working relationship between residential units and their local allied GP surgery have been highlighted (see Part 4, page 77).

These needs assessments go some way to define the obstacles on the pathway to better health for looked after young people. Still to be explored are the views of the young people themselves about access and use of primary health care services.

Staff training

Looking after children and young people away from their homes and parents puts a very high burden of responsibility on those who care. If these young people are particularly vulnerable – with recognised high levels of mental health and behavioural problems, of risk taking activities and from backgrounds of chaotic care within their homes – this requires skill and knowledge on how to recognise problems, where and when to seek help, and how to cope in various situations. If we think realistically about a staff member who works in residential care for 10 years, they will have been involved with many children and young people and will probably have encountered most of the common health and mental health conditions so prevalent in this age group (see Part 2, page 19).

The work of Polnay et al.[29] acknowledged the need for staff support as being one of the main planks to support the move to better health promotion. In their work with young people in residential care in Nottingham Health Care Trust, a model for a residential care training programme was developed. This brought together the expertise of various agencies to work in a truly multi-agency way with social work, to enable young people in local authority community homes to address their own health issues collectively. This model was adopted as one which has been successful in a similar setting before, and became the starting point for the RCHP's work with social work colleagues on staff training.

A study in 1999 by Robinson et al. in Edinburgh, the Care Sick report,[30] described inadequate levels of residential care staff training in areas of health and mental health. These workers also described having inadequate information about health services.

---

[29] Polnay L, et al. Better Health for Children in Residential Care. Arch Dis Child. Sept 1996; 75: 263-265.

[30] Robinson P, et al. Care Sick: The Physical and Mental Health Needs of Looked After and Accommodated Children and Adolescents in Residential Care: Public Health and Inequalities. Young People's Unit, Royal Edinburgh Hospital. Scottish Executive. 1999.

In a study of the psychological problems of looked after and accommodated young people, Chetwynd concluded that training for residential care workers should include a significant proportion of therapeutic child care.[31]

Staff training needs audit

During the initial months of the project, it was clear that staff had very different levels of knowledge and experience regarding health matters. Often, the perceived need for support regarding mental health issues dwarfed the feeling of need for training in other health areas. Help with issues encountered in crisis situations was particularly in demand. So we decided to audit the training needs and wishes of staff in the hope that we could build on their views to provide a service which was both meaningful and included the areas which health professionals felt were essential for carers to be competent in. This was carried out via a staff questionnaire which was delivered to care workers in all units by the RCHP nurses in April 2001.

- 322 questionnaires were delivered and 186 (57.8%) returned
- Respondees had an average length of employment within residential child care of nine years (ranges three months – 30 years, median = 9.25 yrs)

The audit was divided into five broad areas;

- Physical health
- Child health and development
- Mental health and emotional wellbeing
- Health promotion
- Sexual health and relationships

Each subject was then further divided into specific topics. Staff were asked whether they had had training in this area over the past two years and whether they felt they had the knowledge and skills necessary to work with these issues. They were then asked to prioritise three of the health topics listed in which they would most value training. This provided some interesting results, and underpinned the need to support social work management deliver the health component of staff training.

---

31 Chetwynd P, *et al*. Psychological Problems in Young People 'Accommodated' by Glasgow City Council. Greater Glasgow Primary Healthcare NHS Trust. 1999.

PHYSICAL HEALTH

Topic	% trained in last two years	% with little or no skills/ knowledge	% with some skills/knowledge	% with all or most skills/ knowledge required
Asthma/eczema/hay fever, etc.	6	12	56	32
Severe allergies/anaphylaxis	8	56	31	13
Epilepsy	22	27	39	33
Diabetes	8	45	38	45
Meningitis	3	50	34	16
Headlice and other infestations	18	9	32	60
Management of minor ailments	11	7	39	54
Skin problems	2	20	46	34

PRIORITIES FOR TRAINING

Topic	No. choosing this as a priority
Meningitis	84
Epilepsy	83
Severe allergies/anaphylaxis	73
Diabetes	73
Asthma/eczema/hay fever, etc.	68
Management of minor ailments	32
Skin problems	25
Headlice and other infestations	15

All of the topics listed above are likely to be encountered by staff caring for a range of young people over a period of time, and it would be reasonable to expect that a basic knowledge of these should form part of the core training for staff. In some areas where staff had had very little training (for example: asthma, skin problems and management of minor ailments), there was a high feeling of competency in dealing with the problem. This questioned how up-to-date and accurate the knowledge base was which dealt with the issue. And knowledge could be picked up opportunistically, through dealing with individual children, as these conditions are common. In other areas (such as severe anaphylaxis, diabetes and meningitis) there was a clear indication that more staff felt they had inadequate skills or knowledge to deal with the problem.

The top choices for training were meningitis, epilepsy, diabetes and anaphylaxis. Asthma, eczema and hay fever followed closely behind suggesting that, despite the fairly high perceived level of competence among staff in dealing with them, they recognised the need for accurate information about these very common conditions. Prioritisation by staff was in accordance with that of health care staff.

CHILD HEALTH AND DEVELOPMENT

Topic	% trained in last two years	% with little or no skills/ knowledge	% with some skills/ knowledge	% with all or most skills/ knowledge required
Standard health screening/ immunisations	2	42	43	15
Accessing health services for young people	12	22	45	34
Learning/developmental difficulties	8	38	44	18
Normal phases of emotional development/social communication disorders	12	32	42	27
Puberty/growth	17	10	33	57

PRIORITIES FOR TRAINING

Topic	No. choosing this as a priority
Learning/developmental difficulties	96
Normal phases of emotional development/social communication disorders	82
Accessing health services for young people	62
Standard health screening/ immunisations	49
Puberty/growth	42

There was a significant lack of training for staff in learning and developmental disorders, especially considering the recognised poor educational attendance and attainments of the young people. This was matched by large numbers of staff choosing this as a priority area for training. Likewise, there was little prior training about how to access health services for young people, and about normal phases of emotional development and social communication disorders, also prioritised as areas for future training.

MENTAL HEALTH AND EMOTIONAL WELLBEING

Topic	% trained in last two years	% with little or no skills/ knowledge	% with some skills/knowledge	% with all or most skills/ knowledge required
Depression	10	28	54	18
Anxiety	9	20	55	24
Managing aggression and violence	59	6	28	66
Psychosis	3	69	26	5
Attention Deficit Hyperactivity Disorder (ADHD)	8	39	42	19
Attachment disorders	22	36	36	28
Eating disorders	5	35	50	15
Self harm	12	21	53	26
Obsessive compulsive disorder	4	59	28	13
Emotional effects of child abuse	31	11	50	40
Bedwetting/soiling	6	22	48	30
Loss and bereavement	24	18	45	38

PRIORITIES FOR TRAINING

Topic	No. choosing this as a priority
Self harm	44
Attachment disorders	34
Emotional effects of child abuse	32
Psychosis	28
Eating disorders	28
Attention Deficit Hyperactivity Disorder (ADHD)	27
Depression	13
Obsessive compulsive disorder	9
Loss and bereavement	8
Managing aggression and violence	7
Bedwetting/soiling	3
Anxiety	2

By far the most training in this area has previously been directed towards managing aggression and violence, rather than exploring the root problems of mental health and wellbeing. This mirrored the tendency in the past to look for, and to be provided with, support for times of crisis rather than support to improve young people's emotional health in the hope these crises might be fewer. This was appropriately reflected by a very low demand for further training in this area.

The main areas where further training was prioritised were self harm, attachment disorders and emotional effects of child abuse, with eating disorders, ADHD and psychosis close behind. This suggested that staff felt they needed help to understand the complexities of the common situations with which they are regularly faced. Given the huge rates of emotional and behavioural disturbance in the young people cared for (see Part 2, page 20), we felt this highlighted the very real need for staff to have access to high quality advice and training, in an ongoing manner, and to support them to cope with mental health issues (see Part 3, page 49 and Part 5, page 85).

HEALTH PROMOTION

Topic	% trained in last two years	% with little or no skills/ knowledge	% with some skills/knowledge	% with all or most skills/ knowledge required
Dental health	2	16	48	36
First Aid/emergency care	46	6	35	59
Prevention of accidents	22	6	45	49
Smoking	8	5	40	55
Alcohol	10	8	42	49
Drug/solvent misuse	23	13	47	41
HIV/hepatitis	11	26	49	22

PRIORITIES FOR TRAINING

Topic	No. choosing this as a priority
Drug/solvent misuse	104
HIV/hepatitis	98
Alcohol	67
First Aid/emergency care	61
Prevention of accidents	25
Smoking	22
Dental health	18

Almost half of the staff had had some training in First Aid and emergency care, and almost a quarter in accident prevention and drug and solvent misuse. Very few received any training over the past three years in bloodborne diseases (such as HIV, hepatitis), alcohol abuse, smoking or dental health. To develop the health promoting unit (see Part 3, page 45 and Part 5, page 87), it is essential that care staff are supported in how best to talk to young people about healthy living practices.

Training priorities included further training in drug and solvent misuse, blood-borne diseases and alcohol abuse. Further training in First Aid and emergency care was sought by almost a third of the staff. Dental health was not seen as a priority at this stage in the project (near the beginning), and is one area where we have actively sought to raise awareness as some simple measures could have a significant effect on young people's health and self esteem (see Part 5, page 87).

SEXUAL HEALTH AND RELATIONSHIPS

Topic	% trained in last two years	% with little or no skills/ knowledge	% with some skills/knowledge	% with all or most skills/ knowledge required
Promoting self esteem and self confidence	26	6	40	54
Promoting positive relationships	18	5	41	54
Sexual identity	16	15	46	39
Pregnancy and contraception	10	8	47	45
Sexually transmitted infections	12	13	51	37

PRIORITIES FOR TRAINING

Topic	No. choosing this as a priority
Sexual identity	89
Promoting self esteem and self confidence	87
Promoting positive relationships	76
Sexually transmitted infections	66
Pregnancy and contraception	23

Previous training in the area of sexual health and relationships for staff was scant, although this is a subject which most, if not all, residential care staff will have to deal with at some stage in their careers. Staff picked up on the need for training to understand issues of sexual identity, promoting self esteem and positive relationships. A wish for information about sexually transmitted diseases came closely behind. Slightly less than a quarter of respondents requested training in pregnancy and contraception, perhaps reflecting that they identified more with areas in which they can work most effectively to promote good sexual health and wellbeing. Also, it could be argued that carers are more likely to be able to help the young person access specialist services on contraception and pregnancy, should such advice be needed.

Conclusions from staff training audit

Clearly staff have had little or no training on a range of health topics. Staff priorities for training in each area formed the basis of a health training programme which was delivered over a week in February 2002. This training was aimed at the health link workers from each unit (see Part 4, page 137), to start an ongoing programme of health training which could, ultimately, become part of staff development within social work. Project staff also contributed to foundation training (a rolling programme of initial training for all new residential care staff).

Training week

The model of a week of health training was adopted as described in the work of Polnay et al [32] and had many strengths. It was easy to replicate, and was a starting point for a rolling programme of training to suit the needs of individual units. The involvement of other health agencies helped to raise awareness in those agencies of the particular needs of looked after children. A programme for the week was developed by two staff members along with the City of Edinburgh's social work employee development officer. It was based on the staff training audit, and was designed to cover normal child development, the spectrum of health and illness, workers' roles in needs assessment and better use of existing services. No sessions on drugs or drug awareness were included, as there is an established training programme in place on these topics for care staff. The overall aim was to help unit staff to recognise and value their role in health promotion, to identify the supports required to fulfil this role, to provide information on health and health services, and to introduce staff to health service providers.

Thirty workers attended all or part of the week, with 14 attending all the sessions. The enthusiasm and responsiveness of the group was maintained throughout the week, good ideas were exchanged and new ideas explored. The course was positively evaluated by those who attended, unanimously, who found it useful, informative and of great relevance for their work.

Sustainability of health training

It was felt sustainability was vital in terms of ongoing training, and the RCHP has worked very closely with social work to ensure that training initiatives started during the project continue as core staff development. To this end, we have been working with social work management, the employee development officer for Edinburgh, and have consulted with the Scottish Institute of Residential Child Care (SIRCC), based at Strathclyde University, which is the national training centre for residential child care in Scotland.

We would advocate integration of the concept of health link workers, as well as training, into staff development. If each staff member served for a couple of years as a unit health link worker, ensuring that health standards were met for their individual unit, and with the provision of up-to-date health training, the outcome for health promotion and health care for the children and young people would inevitably be improved.

---

32 Polnay L, et al. Better Health for Children in Residential Care. Arch Dis Child. Sept 1996; 75: 263-265.

Part 3 Promoting Better Health

Background

Our beliefs about health are based on the cultures we grew up in and on our life experiences. As workers, our set of assumptions will influence our views of others' behaviours, attitudes or susceptibilities to health problems. The holistic view of health which underpinned the work of the Residential Care Health Project (RCHP) can be summarised in the following World Health Organization definition:

'The extent to which an individual or group is able on the one hand to realise aspirations and satisfy needs and on the other hand to change or cope with the environment. Health is therefore seen as a resource for everyday life, not the object of living; it is a positive concept emphasising social and personal resources as well as physical capabilities.' (WHO, 1984)

Therefore we are concerned not only with prevention of ill health but with actively promoting positive mental, physical and social health.

A residential unit may have 15 to 20 members of staff and six to eight residents, each of whom holds different views on health, so reaching agreement on strategies for health promotion is inevitably difficult. The concept of the 'Health Promoting Unit' was described in 1997 by Polnay *et al.* in the context of promoting better health for children and young people in the care of the local authority in residential units.[1] This model, which was adopted and built on during the RCHP, provided a theoretical framework to aid discussion and to facilitate movement from the abstract to the concrete.

Health promotion has its origins in the narrower field of health education which, up until the 1960s, was primarily concerned with messages about hygiene and limiting the spread of diseases. Against a background of major change in health and education services, holistic views of health have become widely accepted and, from the 1980s, health promotion has been viewed as a serious theoretically based discipline.[2][3] Many models have been developed, and Tannahill's is one which has been widely accepted by health care workers.[4] It provides a helpful framework for identifying health promotion needs and opportunities and also a framework for action planning. Tannahill talks of three overlapping spheres of activity:

- Health education
- Prevention
- Health protection

Health education

Health education may be defined as 'any communication activity aimed at enhancing positive health and preventing or diminishing ill health'.[5] Communication may be between individuals, groups or communities and is influenced by beliefs, attitudes and behaviours. Activities of daily living within residential units present many opportunities for incidental or planned health education interventions. Workers need to place value on their input and recognise their contribution to health promotion.

---

1 Report of the Programme Team for Health Needs of Young People in Residential Care 1992-1997. Nottingham Community Health NHS Trust. The University of Nottingham. 1998.

2 Tannahill A. What is Health Promotion? *Health Educ J.* 1985; 44 (4): 167-168.

3 Tannahill A. Commentary. The Scottish Green Paper: Beyond a Healthy Mind in a Healthy Body. *J Public Health Med.* Sep 1998; 20 (3): 249-252.

4 Tannahill A. Health Promotion and Public Health: a Model in Action. *Community Medicine.* Feb 1998; 10 (1): 48-51.

5 Boddington N, *et al.* The Health Promoting School: Focusing on Health and School Improvement. Forbes Publications. London 1996.

Prevention

Prevention is concerned with reducing or avoiding the risk of diseases and ill health primarily, though not exclusively, through medical interventions. Prevention may operate at several levels – prevention of onset (eg, immunisations), prevention of progression of disease (screening and early detection), prevention of avoidable complications (eg, good diabetes control) or prevention of recurrence (eg, dental check-ups). Record keeping, care planning, review and appropriate use of health services all contribute to reducing the risk of ill health.

Health protection

Health protection is about safeguarding population health through legal, fiscal or social measures. Examples of this include the development of legislation regarding seatbelts and drink driving, raising tax on tobacco and alcohol, and the enforcement of 'no smoking' policies in public places. Policies within social work also at unit level have a health protection function, for example health and safety regulations, staff training and supervision.

The World Health Organization (WHO) has been a major driving force behind the development of health promotion. The idea of health promoting schools emerged from a movement labelled by the WHO as a 'settings approach'. Schools are seen as an agency for socialising each new generation and the philosophy of health promotion is at the core of a healthy school.[6][7]

The key features of a health promoting school can be seen to apply quite naturally to residential units. Focus on raising self esteem through active participation, developing skills and reducing risk of failure should be central to relationships between staff and young people, and it is important to recognise that skills and processes are common to all health issues. Resident meetings, time with key workers and normal social interaction all provide opportunities for young people to participate in decision making. Negotiating skills can be learned which are essential for life and for the development of more secure relationships, better mental and sexual health and more appropriate use of health services. Ultimately these skills manifest themselves in better adjusted adults who can secure employment and live more fulfilling lives.

It may be helpful to look at the elements of health promotion around a specific health related topic:

Diet and nutrition are concerned with more than providing basic knowledge on the components of a healthy diet. Developing skills in choosing and preparing food, budgeting and storing food safely are also required (education). Having a healthy choice of food available, and knowledge and management of food allergies is also necessary (prevention). Regulations on food labelling or use of chemicals in food production is a responsibility for policy makers at a national level (protection).

The same principles apply to living with a condition such as asthma or diabetes; knowledge of the illness and how to minimise its effects, access to services and the resources allocated to treatment and management are all features of health promotion.

---

6 Jensen BB. Health Knowledge and Health Education in the Democratic Health-Promoting School. *Health Education.* Jul/Aug 2000; 100 (4): 146-153.

7 Rasmussen VB, *et al.* The European Network of Health Promoting Schools: An Alliance of Health, Education and Democracy. *Health Education.* Mar 2000; 100 (2): 61-67.

The activities of the RCHP team have been concerned mainly with health education and prevention, aimed primarily at carers. This was deliberate, and developed in recognition of the fact that this particular group of young people may be very wary of strangers, while acknowledging the crucial role that parents and carers play within the home in the promotion of better health for the children they care for. Supporting the care staff by providing information, training, advice and consultation has helped to prioritise health within units. Comprehensive health assessments carried out by the team paediatrician identified previously undiagnosed problems which could then be addressed. Improved systems for health assessments at the point of being looked after and accommodated, better use of primary care services and development of core health records which support the use of 'Looked After Children' materials all contribute to health promotion for children and young people in residential care.

Although the main thrust of health education and health promotion support in the RCHP has been directed towards residential care workers, in areas such as drug, alcohol and volatile substance misuse and sexual health, specialist agencies have provided excellent educational services directly to the young people (see Part 3, page 49 and page 102; Part 5, page 85 and page 86). At all times a flexible approach was required, considering the dynamics of individual units and the appropriateness of group or individual work in relation to the population of the units, relationships within units, wishes of young people and, most importantly, what was currently happening in their lives. Flexibility may also be required regarding whether individual workers are best equipped to do specific health promotion work. Young people may feel uncomfortable discussing certain issues with workers of the opposite sex, for example, and some workers may feel frankly uncomfortable dealing with certain topics.

The measures initiated to promote better health within units come alongside national drives within social work and education to improve the health of young people generally. In most areas of the country initiatives aimed at increasing opportunities for access to sport and leisure and to implement healthier living standards are being developed. During the course of the RCHP these developments were impacting on units in Edinburgh, East Lothian and Midlothian, underlining the fact that the responsibility for good health does not lie with any one agency, but with all of us, in all aspects of our lives.

The role of the nurses in promoting better health

Before formulating interventions to improve the health outcomes of children and young people in residential care, it was necessary to have an infrastructure which could underpin the entire project; a health resource which could be easily accessible to all staff and young people in the residential care system, whilst having reliable links to other health service providers. This resource required channels of communication with Health and Social Work personnel at all levels, from service providers to the highest strategists, if sustainable change was to be implemented.

The project was based on a network of four nurses, central to the RCHP team. The work of these nurses within their named units was central to building interagency relationships and linking to the many other health service providers. Links to more strategic levels of the various agencies was achieved through the project steering group and the project director.

The four nurses, comprising two whole-time equivalent staff members, were employed as a team, and came from very different backgrounds – school nursing, primary care, special needs and community education – with diverse perspectives and experience. The formation of specific task groups (on immunisation, staff training, dental health, sexual health, for example) allowed individuals to utilise their particular expertise to the full, with agreement that initiatives being developed for the units had to be consistent throughout the project. Overall, a supportive and understanding team was formed.

During the early stages of the project considerable time was spent reviewing the available research and literature. This gave an understanding of the key issues impacting on the health of the young people. However, it only gave limited insight into the day-to-day realities of residential care. So considerable time was spent meeting with staff and young people, primarily with designated health link workers nominated by the units as the main contact for all health-related matters (see Part 4, page 77). This was invaluable. It gave the opportunity for relationships to be built and allowed, in time, for open and honest discussions to be had. Link workers described the enormity of the issues facing the young people and highlighted how this often translated into high levels of risk taking behaviour. They often described a pattern of unplanned and inappropriate care placements, and spoke of pressurised work environments with staffing shortages that negated health training and support opportunities. Health often appeared to be a low priority. Indeed, health initiatives were most often crisis-led and there was often an undercurrent of frustration towards health service providers who were unable to meet the perceived needs of the young people. Armed with this greater understanding, the nurses were able to develop their roles more appropriately.

The key aim was to raise health as a priority issue, and to support and encourage staff to take a more active approach towards health issues. It was hoped that young people could be encouraged to become interested in their health, and advised on healthier lifestyle choices. The aim was also to raise the awareness of health care providers to the particular needs of this disadvantaged group and to encourage developments that would improve access to health care services.

The nursing role therefore targeted three levels:
- Young people
- Residential care staff
- Service providers

Also vital was the implementation of the various audits which were necessary to assess the situation at the start of the project regarding records in units (see Part 2, page 27) and staff training needs (see Part 2, page 35).

Involvement with young people

Initial contact with young people in units was, of necessity, very informal – for example, dropping in to units to meet whoever was there at the time or joining the group for the evening meal. Direct work with young people tended to be opportunistic rather than planned.

During the first few months of the project, young people were invited to meet with the nurses for an informal chat. A loose structure, set around a questionnaire purely aimed at 'ice breaking', helped the nurses to gain a better understanding of the views of young people about their health, fitness and interests, and tried to establish who was important in their day-to-day lives in terms of health management. This would help the entire project develop those services most appropriate to meet the needs of the young people. It also started the young people thinking about health more holistically in the context of fitness, interests and wellbeing.

Forty-two young people met with their unit nurses during the early months. They seemed a group with a very 'normal' spread of interests for their age, and the importance to them of those caring for them in the units was very obvious. 81% stated that they enjoyed sports, when they had the opportunity, with football, basketball and swimming coming out as the favourites. A wide range of interests was mentioned, including skating, gymnastics, running, skiing and riding, while 50% expressed a desire for more access to sport and leisure facilities. Only 15 (36%) felt that they ate a healthy diet, underlined by one comment: *'Well, it's chips and chips and chips and fish!'.*

Young people were asked whom they would approach if they felt unwell or unhappy. If unwell, 81% said they would approach a unit staff member (63% would go to any member of staff and 18% would approach their keyworker) while 13% said they would approach no one.

If unhappy, young people were more likely to approach their keyworker (34%), with a further 24% going to any member of staff. Of the 29 young people who responded to this question, 27% said that they would not go to anyone. *Only one young person said that they would seek help from a family member.* None mentioned their Social Worker.

Finally, young people were asked to list any subjects they wanted help with and the nurses offered to meet with them later to discuss these. A wide range of issues was put forward, including very appropriate concerns about family history of serious medical conditions (breast cancer and coronary heart disease), smoking, alcohol, drugs, dental health and skin care.

Once an understanding developed of life within a YPC, the role of the nurses evolved. Before the project started, it was envisaged that the nurses would be active in carrying out clinical work (for example doing immunisations, running drop-in clinics) but as time went on this was not considered to be the most effective way of working. Bearing in mind the wish that the young people should have exactly the same opportunities for health care as those who live at home with their parents, the most appropriate use of nursing time became facilitating links with health service providers, supporting staff and young people to have a full knowledge of available resources and how to make the best possible use of these. There was a level of 1:1 health promotion, often needs led, and a certain amount of group work was carried out. At all times it had to be remembered that the units are the current homes of the young people and the appropriateness of certain health promotional activities in this setting had to be considered.

It became obvious early on that, for health information to be given to young people, it would be most appropriately delivered by adequately trained and supported staff, at a time which was right for the young person. This view was underlined by the initial nurse interviews with young people, when they largely identified unit staff as their chosen support in times of need.

The nurses developed an advisory role, similar to that adopted by health visitors with the under 5s. At the very early stages of a child's life, parents need advice and support about conditions and concerns of which they have no former experience, hence the need for this type of nursing support. In residential care, the situation is very similar. A carer may, with little or no notice, have to care for a child or young person with a condition they have never encountered before. Therefore the nurses' role with young people evolved largely into one of advising and supporting those who care for them.

Finally, the nurses worked closely with the project paediatrician and were responsible for arranging comprehensive health assessments (see Part 2, page 12), following up the health recommendations made at these assessments and helping staff to implement recommended interventions leading to improved health outcomes.

Involvement with residential care staff

Considerably more time was given to providing support, advice and guidance to staff in their own work with the young people, and helping them access available health care services. When developing health initiatives a joint working approach was fostered, ensuring that staff groups participated in all stages of planning and organisation. This encouraged the view of health as everybody's responsibility and helped develop the skills and confidence of Social Work staff in delivering health promotion and health education messages. Over time, individual care planning began to take over from continual crisis management.

Many issues of care and service were identified as causing barriers to good practice, and much joint working was aimed at minimising the effects of, for example, difficulties with communication, shift systems and staffing crises. There were challenges for the nurses in working in the environment of another professional group, and also in working with young people in what, for the time being, was their home. These difficulties were eased, to a degree, by gaining a better understanding of each other's work remit, and by mutual respect and trust. However, both agencies recognise that interagency working is of prime importance and that neither agency can, alone, deliver the best health care for these young people.

Individual work with staff has focused around training and support, with the nurses central to planning a programme of health training for care staff. The successful return of 186 staff training needs assessment audit forms (see Part 2, page 36) was largely the result of the presence of familiar health workers within the units.

Involvement with service providers

As well as supporting care staff to access health services for young people, considerable effort had to go into educating service providers outwith the RCHP of the specific needs of these children and young people. The nurses, therefore, took on an advocacy role for the young people with various health service providers, including community child health, primary care, dental, mental and sexual health services. The general finding was that most health service providers outwith community child health had no understanding of the reasons underlying the difficulties in delivering health care to young people in the care system, but were willing to adopt a more flexible approach to ensure better uptake of services when the facts were explained. This has brought about significant changes in the delivery of some services, with a flexibility which ensures that, if the standard way of accessing a service cannot be achieved, an approach which will reach the young people can be adopted.

Largely as a result of the challenges of this area of work, and the isolation felt about informed nursing advice regarding the needs of looked after children, the nurses established a Scottish nurses' special interest group. This has brought together nurses from all over Scotland, to network on a national level throughout Scotland and the UK.

Conclusion

The nursing infrastructure has been central to the success and development of the project. With the Residential Care Health Project nurses coming from a variety of backgrounds, there has always been eager debate on all issues presented, with the underlying commitment to the wellbeing of the young people. It has been this debate which has led to the development of long-term strategies for change. The introduction of various mechanisms to improve communication (for example, health link worker system) enabled the development of valuable relationships between the nurses and social work colleagues. This allowed a clearer insight into the lives of the young people and led the team to look critically at mainstream health service provision which so often does not meet the needs of this vulnerable group. It has been possible to use this critical analysis in order to instigate positive change for the benefit of the young people.

Mental health

'I didn't even have my teddy.'

Young girl, 13, following emergency admission to a young people's centre

'You can't go too slow in forming a relationship with these young people, but you can go too fast.'

Mental health practitioner, Residential Care Health Project

Introduction

The analysis of the Comprehensive Health Assessments (CHAs) of 105 children and young people looked after and accommodated in young people's centres during the Residential Care Health Project (see Part 2, page 25) confirmed very high rates of emotional, behavioural and mental health problems among the cohort. 101 of the young people (97%) were assessed by the paediatrician as having difficulties of a degree that would merit referral on to mental health services for further advice. Although these figures were the result of clinical assessment by a paediatrician and not a psychiatrist, the results mirrored those of past research.[8][9][10] When consideration is given to the life histories of the young people, the high incidence is not particularly surprising as many have well documented risk factors for the development of mental health problems in adult life.[11][12][13][14][15]

In Edinburgh in 1999, the Care Sick report[16] identified that 85% of a sample of young people in residential care, interviewed in focus groups, were highly impaired socially and functionally by their difficulties, based on self-rating and carer ratings. Depression scores on the Moods and Feelings Questionnaire[17] were roughly 40% higher than that of the local adolescent population and the group made repeated reference to their feelings of insecurity and high stress levels. Young people and staff caring for them had limited information and knowledge about the nature of mental health problems, and misinformation was apparent in both groups.

Following the appointment of the mental health worker to the RCHP in January 2001, a study looked at contact with mental health services by the current population of young people in residential care.[18] Of 105 young people in YPCs in January 2001, 56% had already had contact with mental health services and 14.3% were in current contact. Risk factors for adult mental health problems were common (average 3.01 risk factors per child). Although the levels of referral were high, the diagnostic basis for referral had largely the same distribution as a community sample of referrals to child and adolescent mental health services.

8 McCann JB, *et al*. Prevalence of Psychiatric Disorders in Young People in the Care System. *BMJ*. Dec 1996; 313: 1529-1530.

9 Dimigen G, *et al*. Psychiatric Disorder Among Young Children at the Time of Entering Local Authority Care: Questionnaire Survey. *BMJ*. Sept 1999; 319: 675.

10 Chetwynd P, *et al*. Psychological Problems in Young People 'Accommodated' by Glasgow City Council. Greater Glasgow Primary Healthcare NHS Trust. 1999.

11 Schneiderman. Mental Health Services for Children in Out of Home Care. *Child Welfare*. 1998; LXXVII (1): 29-39.

12 Garland AF, *et al*. Types of Maltreatment as a Predictor of Mental Health Service Use for Children in Foster Care. *Child Abuse & Neglect*. Aug 1996; 20 (8): 675-688.

13 Stein E. Mental Health of Children in Foster Care: A Comparison with Community and Clinical Samples. *Canadian Journal of Psychiatry*. Aug 1996; 41 (6): 385-391.

14 Hamilton CE. Continuity and Discontinuity of Attachment from Infancy Through Adolescence. *Child Development*. May/June 2000; 71 (3): 690-694.

15 Cantos AL, *et al*. Correlates of Therapy Referral in Foster Children. *Child Abuse & Neglect*. Oct 1996; 20 (10): 921-931.

16 Robinson P, *et al*. Care Sick: The Physical and Mental Health Needs of Looked After and Accommodated Children and Adolescents in Residential Care: Public Health and Inequalities. Young People's Unit, Royal Edinburgh Hospital. Scottish Executive. 1999.

17 Angold A, *et al*. Development of a Short Questionnaire for Use in Epidemiological Studies of Depression in Children and Adolescents. *International Journal of Methods in Psychiatric Research*. Dec 1995; 5 (4): 237-249.

18 Perry M. University of Edinburgh Special Studies Module 2001. A Study of the Contact of Children in Residential Care with Mental Health Services. (unpublished). 2001.

At the outset of the project, preliminary general discussions took place between the RCHP director and staff in units to explain the aims and implementation of the project. Mental health issues were consistently identified by management and practitioners as the single most pressing area needing support in their task of helping young people in the units. Many factors were reported to contribute to the difficulties in managing mental health and behavioural problems within the residential care setting. Some related to the young people themselves, some involved the units and staffing within units, some concerned field social work supports, and some were firmly rooted in a lack of mental health resources with subsequent difficulties in accessing help.

Factors relating to the young people

- Difficulty in engaging young people, especially when seen by an unfamiliar adult
- Lack of trust
- Issues around confidentiality
- Prevalence of co-morbidity, especially acting out or externalising behaviours which may mask underlying anxiety or depression
- Young people's unwillingness to attend specialist mental health services
- Lack of a close confidant within the unit
- Units can sometimes feel frightening, with young people concentrating on survival with high levels of anxiety and arrested emotional development

Factors relating to units

- Carers' lack of training in mental health issues and available services
- Ethos of 'containment'
- Ethos of 'crisis management'
- Shift systems and ensuing lack of consistency
- Carers' own personal feelings and difficulties in engaging with particularly challenging young people
- Carers' 'burn out' from often seemingly relentless exposure to extremely difficult children and young people

Factors relating to field social workers/social services

- Staffing levels and availability of social workers to engage in therapeutic work with young people
- Frequent changes of social worker
- Lack of awareness and training in adolescent mental health issues
- Difficulties in attending training, even when offered, due to staffing levels or crises

Factors relating to health services

- Lack of resources
- Lack of personnel with experience of the very specific needs of young people in the care system and those who care for them
- Centralisation of resources
- Lack of flexibility
- Reluctance of mental health services to get involved because of 'unstable care situation'
- Difficulties in using local resources (including primary care, school- and community-based resources) due to frequent moves, poor school attendance, lack of connections

One of the most important aspects of the RCHP, therefore, was to examine the whole question of the need for mental health support and advice, to look at the current situation and to make recommendations for a more robust support service for the future. A half-time mental health worker was therefore employed to look at areas such as working with residential carers, training, consultation, liaison between units and child and adolescent mental health services, and direct work with young people.

It became apparent that mental health is viewed very differently by Child and Adolescent Mental Health Services (CAMHS) and residential care workers. This includes the language to describe mental health, the views about the cause of problems and the type of support treatment which is felt to be appropriate. Mental health services, for example, are seen to use terms such as *mental illness or disorder,* while social workers refer to *mental health issues or problems.*

Of the young people seen by the paediatrician (Part 2, page 25), 42% had undergone treatment in the past for mental health problems while 19% were currently being seen at CAMHS. A further 11% were referred urgently and 11% non-urgently to tertiary CAMHS. Carers expressed frustration that referrals to tertiary services were sometimes not accepted because the young person *'needs to be settled in a stable placement before work can be done',* or a mental illness was not deemed to be present. They were concerned that young people could be seen only once and then discharged. They commented that *'the assessment is often too short for a formulation to be considered',* and that they (CAMHS) … *'don't know the young person like we do'.* Mental health services are often perceived to be closing the door on these young people. One manager, who stated that four of her former residents had been admitted to a psychiatric hospital in the months and years after they left her care, wondered if more could have been done for these young people during their formative years to prevent this happening.

Young people seen by CAMHS have a thorough assessment of their mental state, circumstances, and personal and family history. If a mental illness is not present (such as depression, ADHD, eating disorder, psychotic illness), work will not usually be continued. Many of the young people on the units presented with emotional, behavioural and relationship difficulties rather than primary mental illness, and therefore tools such as those which measure rates of mental health disorder in the general population may prove inadequate here. These high levels of psychosocial impairment often mask huge levels of anxiety and distress, reflecting the most disturbed, violent and abusive early lives, and are frequently the precursors to significant adult mental health problems.

When young people have been seen by CAMHS, mental health professionals will normally make recommendations for care, on the understanding that these will be undertaken. The most appropriate recommendation for many will be good standard care, understanding and the building of relationships, trust and self esteem within the unit. The main thrust of the consultation on these occasions may be simply to reassure staff that the work they are already doing is the best for these young people.

Sometimes, however, this can be difficult to achieve within units. It may be completely outwith the control of staff, as a result of staffing levels or changes, or because of admission policies causing disruption among previously stable groups of young people. CAMHS staff may not be aware of the constant day-to-day stress that life at a YPC may pose for staff in terms of coping with the constant crises and disruptions which are present when working with such extremely vulnerable young people. As one RCHP staff member said, *'They're so often either in the middle of a crisis or recovering from the one the day before'.* It was invaluable to gain first-hand experience of life on a YPC to understand the challenges posed, and to appreciate the difficulties at times of working through planned interventions.

Sometimes, difficulty in providing appropriate care for a young person may be due to a lack of understanding among the staff that the way they feel or behave lies clearly in the detail of their life history or present circumstances. It is important that CAMHS staff remember that for staff dealing with such extreme degrees of emotional and behavioural difficulties, these underlying theories of behaviour must be explained. An example which was frequently to the fore was the difficulty that many young people experienced at bed time. Often, on looking back at the young person's experiences, there had been a degree of violence or abuse particularly at bed time. The difficulties could also be explained by the fear and anxieties of being in a strange place at night with adults and young people who were not familiar to them. One young girl expressed well why she was distressed and could not sleep at night – *'It's the only time I get to think'*. If this is the case, simple bedtime management techniques may well fail without considering the other factors.

Care practitioners are frequently unclear about what CAMHS has to offer, probably due to a lack of direct contact other than when working with specific cases or at times of crisis. The carers' expectations ranged from an unrealistic view of the power and possibilities of therapy to simply wishing to confirm or eliminate anything more serious. Residential care practitioners tended not to have accessed previously available resources, such as telephone consultations with CAMHS, and most were unaware of referral criteria to CAMHS. The situation was often true in reverse, with CAMHS staff having unrealistic expectations of care practitioners' knowledge of mental health issues, and lacking understanding of the realities of working in a YPC.

Between the sides in this polarisation is a no-man's-land where, given adequate resources, social work and CAMHS might work together more effectively. Here there are many young people who are emotionally troubled but not mentally ill, for whom CAMHS referral criteria currently do not apply. Care staff feel they are ill prepared to help these young people and desperately seek support and advice.

Mental health support from the RCHP mental health practitioner therefore evolved into the following broad area:

- Consultation with staff about young people
- Liaison between units and CAMHS
- Direct work with young people
- Training
- Helping the RCHP staff to understand unit staff's difficulties in working with very troubled young people

Initially, contact was made with every unit manager or assistant manager, to discuss the mental health worker's role and the units' expectations. Fortunately, there was no discrepancy between what was being offered and what was being sought. Obviously, with only 0.5 whole-time equivalent mental health worker for 17 units, it was impossible to offer a comprehensive service so, after the introductions, work in units was needs led. Much of this work focused on finding the most effective use of the limited input from a dedicated mental health resource.

RCHP mental health practitioner consultation with staff about children and young people

Consultations were generally requested because of concern about a specific young person. This was not necessarily due to an obvious mental health problem, but frequently as a result of what staff described as 'bizarre behaviour', 'very odd behaviour', 'unusual behaviour', 'aggression', 'vulnerability' or 'self-harming behaviour'.

The process involved meeting with the keyworker to talk through the present problems, usually for between an hour and an hour and a half. The young person's history was discussed, to try to find an explanation for their present behaviour. Good descriptions by workers could be very illuminating, allowing valid consultancy to be done without direct work with young people.

Recurring themes included the fact that help tended to be sought rather late in the day, when things were so out of control that a secure placement was ultimately going to be the only answer. Great faith was placed in counselling as having a magical effect – *'if only this young person could have counselling'* and *'if only this young person could have impulse control work'.* In many cases these young people did not want counselling or impulse control work, and it could be exceptionally difficult to offer help to young people who did not wish to engage.

Frequently work was done with staff around inconsistencies of management of young people, working with them to understand the processes and to make sense of what was happening. An example was the use of restraint, with workers using it in different ways, at different times and for different criteria. Discussions around the need for uniformity from all staff members at all times helped to mould more consistent limit setting, which was more straightforward and understandable to young people.

Staff frequently felt powerless, threatened, bullied and harassed by children and young people. They appeared to be overwhelmed with the way young people treated them at times, with difficulties in understanding the psychological processes that occur within these transactions. Contact with parents can bring about many traumas and disappointments for young people in the care system, either through being 'let down' by parents not turning up, or through frustration at the inability of parents to meet the needs of the young person. Sometimes, young people could put workers in the role of their parents and then be very angry with them, with counter-transference issues. Workers could become defensive, with their ability to give care affected by distancing from the young person. Defence mechanisms within staff which arose from the situations they found themselves in could be quite damaging, thus escalating the whole cycle of events.

Many consultations involved discussion on how to manage the young people – for example looking at key flashpoints of behaviour, at triggers for difficult behaviour, and bedtime routines. Staff were helped to understand the need to listen rather than to react, and how to choose the right way and the right time to speak with young people.

This way, support was given to staff working with young people who may not have been felt to have a mental illness – for whom psychiatric services would not have been forthcoming – but who actually need more support than workers in residential care can normally provide. Frequently, behaviours felt to be 'bizarre', actually fitted with the kinds of lifestyles the young people had had, and what they were displaying could be understood as adapted coping mechanisms rather than odd, obscure or psychotic behaviour patterns. Often, one consultation was enough for workers to come to a conclusion.

RCHP mental health practitioner liaison between YPCs and mental health services

Sometimes, in the course of consultation, it became apparent that a referral was required to CAMHS. In these cases it was helpful for the RCHP mental health practitioner to liaise with CAMHS as there was a better understanding of the special needs of young people in the care system and of their carers. This led to more effective working between CAMHS and units. The mental health role within the RCHP has enabled CAMHS to understand better the particular needs of looked after children in terms of their mental health. There has been an acceptance that, due to the complex needs of these young people, a dedicated resource is required for looked after children and young people. The RCHP mental health practitioner, in many ways, took on the role of advocate for children and young people in residential care as far as CAMHS services were concerned.

Direct work with young people

Due to time constraints, only a very limited amount of work was carried out with young people by the RCHP mental health worker. This tended to be in the context of observing behaviours to support consultation work.

However, following the health assessments by the paediatrician (see Part 2, page 25), several young people were referred for individual support or counselling to other agencies – for example: school-based support teams, drug and alcohol counselling, bereavement counselling, post abuse counselling and to youth workers. The young people's social workers or keyworkers were the most commonly used resource to provide one-to-one support when needed.

Training

In the area of mental health, training was undertaken within individual units and at formal staff training opportunities, both foundation training and at the health training week.

In units

This was generally carried out on request, the feedback from carers suggesting that it was greatly appreciated, with staff feeling heard, understood and personally supported. Teaching topics included general mental illness, mental health services and how to access them, adolescent development, staff dynamics and how young people made workers feel. Staff were encouraged to use existing mental health consultation services, and were advised which conditions could be best helped by the mental health services and how best to prepare information for consultations. In one unit, a series of eight planned sessions, arranged with the unit nurse, was well received and evaluated.

Problems of training within units included:

- Issues within the unit resulting in too few staff available
- Interruptions
- Lack of direction due to informality

These could, with some difficulty, be resolved but formal training of staff, other than that arising out of individual consultations, was generally felt to be best achieved outwith the units.

Formal staff training

Formal training in mental health (see Part 2, page 40) was offered to 30 health link workers at the health training week, which covered child health and development, mental health and emotional wellbeing, access to health services, and health promotion. The RCHP has been working with social services to make this an integral part of residential care staff career development. The training week followed a staff training audit (see Part 2, page 35), where staff were asked to comment on previous training in health-related matters and also asked to assess their confidence in dealing with the following mental health issues:

- Depression
- Anxiety
- Managing aggression and violence
- Psychosis
- Attention Deficit Hyperactivity Disorder (ADHD)
- Attachment disorders
- Eating disorders
- Self harm
- Obsessive-compulsive disorder
- Emotional effects of child abuse
- Bedwetting and soiling
- Loss and bereavement

Staff were then asked to prioritise their wishes for further training.

By far the most training in this area had previously been directed towards the management of aggression and violence. This seemed to be recognised by staff, with training on self harm, attachment disorders and emotional effects of child abuse coming top, followed by eating disorders, ADHD and psychosis.

Training on mental health matters therefore focused on the issues most relevant to staff, working closely with the social work management and personnel development officer to plan ongoing training for staff.

Helping the RCHP staff to understand unit staff's experiences when working with young people

Any team drawn from a background of differing experience and training, albeit within the health service, brings with it different working methods and standards. It was a big enough task for the entire RCHP to understand each others' roles and areas of responsibilities at the outset, let alone to work out how best to operate within another agency, where staff were, on a daily basis, dealing with young people displaying such difficult behaviours that they could feel powerless and harassed even by quite small children. When involved in work of this nature, it is not only important to help staff to understand the young people, but also to highlight to other agencies (such as health services) the stresses of working life for units staff. This role, although not officially part of the remit of the mental health practitioner, also falls naturally upon anyone working within units whose task it is to explain the extremes of behaviour of some of the resident young people.

An understanding of the problems unit staff face made it easier to work with carers to address some of the problems arising from organising health care amid the general chaos of working with very troubled young people.

The future

Several lessons have been learned through the experience of delivering mental health and behavioural management supports to young people looked after and accommodated in residential care.

- Mental health problems are viewed very differently by residential care practitioners and CAMHS
- The rate of emotional, behavioural and mental health problems is enormous
- The problems cannot be looked at in isolation from the life experiences of the young people
- Standard mental health services, either in the community or in tertiary care, do not serve these young people well
- Carers face a relentless task in trying to help these young people
- Working to improve the health of young people looked after and accommodated by the local authority has revealed a huge unmet need in terms of mental health
- Social work and CAMHS can work together more effectively to support these young people
- Given the risk factors for adult mental illness, these young people, if unsupported, could form a vast pool of adults dependent on mental health service

The RCHP has worked with CAMHS and public health to look at the need for mental health supports at all levels for these young people. A tiered approach of support for young people and their carers has been developed in the City of Edinburgh, following the project. A dedicated mental health team provides training, support and consultation for staff, and assessment and support for individual young people. There are links with tertiary services for those with mental illnesses, and the team works closely with social work, education and the newly appointed nurse for looked after children.

The future should hold out more hope for these young people whose lives have been so damaged by the lottery of their births, compounded by the unnatural surroundings of corporate care. It may not be possible to right all the wrongs but, with the correct supports, we can help give these young people a better chance to become more fulfilled and contented adults.

Sexual health

Background

The Scottish Executive document *Towards a Healthier Scotland*[19] acknowledges that health services have found it hard to tackle the issue of sexual health involving, as it does, physical and emotional need, self-respect and respect for others, as well as risk of infection and disease. Immense concern is raised about the high rate of unwanted teenage pregnancies, many of which occur among the most deprived members of the population. Good sexual health is firmly placed in the domain of a healthy lifestyle, and it is emphasised that sexually transmitted diseases are damaging but preventable.

When considering how best to intervene to support the young people in residential care to achieve better standards of sexual health, and to be more in control of the choices they make regarding sexual activity and risk of unwanted pregnancy, we have taken a very broad look at the whole area. Debate is ongoing as to the efficacy of health education programmes in changing young people's sexual behaviours,[20][21][22] but particularly for those from vulnerable backgrounds, we felt that it was necessary to look much more holistically at the situation. We paid special attention to the characteristics and life experiences of the group of young people, and rather than ask ourselves 'Why do those young people take risks with sexual activity?' we asked 'Why do many young people not take risks with sexual behaviour?'

Sexual risk-taking can obviously result in regret and unhappiness, unwanted pregnancy, sexually transmitted disease and long-term consequences for health and fertility. In their paper *Teenage Fertility and Life Chances*[23] Wellings *et al.* discuss many issues relating to the socio-economic and lifestyle factors of women who become pregnant in their teens. Teenage mothers and their children face poorer prospects in life than do women who delay motherhood until later in life and patterns of early childbearing tend to be repeated in subsequent generations. Poor educational attainment is recognised as an important predictor of early fertility, although it is unclear to what extent pregnancy thwarts academic ambition or to what extent poor academic attainments and expectations lead to a need to seek alternative fulfilment. In the same paper, it states that young people for whom one or both parents are absent are more likely to become parents in early life. However, the most important factor of family life determining the chances of teenage motherhood appears to be the quality of communication about sexual matters within the home. There is also an association with young women from more deprived areas of the country. Those effects are independent of one another, therefore there is a need to intervene at several points in the lives of young women to effect change.

[19] Towards A Healthier Scotland: A White Paper on Health. Scottish Executive. 1999.

[20] Wight D, *et al.* Limits of Teacher Delivered Sex Education: Interim Behavioural Outcomes from Randomised Trial. *BMJ.* Jun 2002; 324: 1430.

[21] DiCenso A, *et al.* Interventions to Reduce Unintended Pregnancies Among Adolescents: Systematic Review of Randomised Controlled Trials. *BMJ.* Jun 2002; 324: 1426.

[22] Graham A, *et al.* Improving Teenagers' Knowledge of Emergency Contraception: Cluster Randomised Controlled Trial of a Teacher Led Intervention. *BMJ.* May 2002; 324: 1179.

[23] Wellings K, *et al.* Teenage Fertility and Life Chances. *Reprod.* Sep 1999; 4 (3): 184-190.

[24] Olausson PO, *et al.* Teenage Childbearing and Long-Term Socioeconomic Consequences: A Case Study in Sweden. *Fam Plann Perspect.* Mar/Apr 2001; 33 (2): 70.

[25] Mirowsky J, *et al.* Depression, Parenthood, and Age at First Birth. *Soc Sci Med.* Apr 2002; 54 (8): 1281-1289.

Childbearing during adolescence poses a risk for socioeconomic disadvantage in later life even for those from relatively comfortable backgrounds,[24] but the age of early pregnancy and experience of childhood poverty are clearly associated with adverse outcomes in adulthood. Early first birth is associated with more feelings and signs of depression in adults, and may reflect a disordered transition from adolescence into adult life, with life-long consequences that influence emotional wellbeing.[25]

As far as sexually transmitted infection is concerned, again there are links with populations who tend to be disadvantaged and marginalised, and who may have limited access to health care.[26] Also, when comparing patients with a sexually transmitted disease (STD) to those without STD, multiple types of abuse and negative life events increased the risk of STD infection, possibly by increasing the likelihood of multiple sexual partners.[27]

The situation regarding sexual behaviour within the cohort of the RCHP was looked at during the comprehensive health assessments by the paediatrician (see Part 2, page 22).

Questions regarding sexual activity were asked in the context of a health assessment, and several young people chose not to respond.

Of those who did:
- 33 (31%) of the 105 assessed by the paediatrician admitted to sexual activity
- Age of youngest person admitting to sex = 12.8 (girl). Age range 12.8-17.2
- Of the 33 admitting to being sexually active, 16 had unsafe sex sometimes, eight always and nine refused to answer. Not one young person stated that they had always been protected when having sex
- 15 young people were referred for screening for sexually transmitted diseases

Of the 44 girls seen, four (9%) were known to be, or to have been, pregnant:
- One was pregnant but miscarried at 22 weeks
- Two had terminations of pregnancy
- One pregnancy was ongoing

Supporting young people in residential care to achieve better sexual health

Structures to get started

In recognition of the concerns voiced in *Towards a Healthier Scotland*,[28] the government set up the demonstration project *Healthy Respect* in Lothian, aimed at promoting sexual health through improving self esteem and respecting others, preventing sexually transmitted diseases, and reducing the number of unwanted pregnancies, especially among teenagers. This project brought together 12 different component projects, all working within separate, but often overlapping areas such as teenage sexual health advice and counselling, contraceptive advice, support for gay, lesbian and transsexual youngsters and young men's health issues. One of the areas identified for particular attention was that of sexual health promotion for young people who are looked after and accommodated by the local authority. Discussions between the RCHP and *Healthy Respect* at the outset resulted in a service level agreement that, for the young people in residential care, *Healthy Respect* and the RCHP

---

[26] Low N, *et al.* Success and Failure in Gonorrhoea Control. *Dermatol Clin.* Oct 1998; 16 (4): 713-722.

[27] Pitzner JK, *et al.* A History of Abuse and Negative Life Events in Patients with a Sexually Transmitted Disease and in a Community Sample. *Child Abuse & Neglect.* May 2000; 24 (5): 715-731.

[28] Towards A Healthier Scotland: A White Paper on Health. Scottish Executive. 1999.

would merge in a symbiotic relationship. In essence *Healthy Respect*, through its various partners, would provide specialist support, advice and materials, and the RCHP would provide the infrastructure and knowledge of the young people, units and carers to enable work to take place.

What did we do?

We started by looking at the many factors which cause responsible attitudes in young people towards sexual health and then considered, in a completely open-minded way, how these factors could be addressed for our particular group of young people. Searching for the factors which protect young people against risk taking, with a view to enhancing good practice, we identified:

- Parental support and family values
- The young person – education and goals
- The young person's emotional wellbeing
- Control of other risk-taking behaviours, for example alcohol consumption, drug taking
- Good formal health education programmes
- Peer behaviour
- Media guidance

Parental support and family values

Generally, the birth parents for this group of young people have been poor role models in their early lives. The young people often come from a background of abuse or neglect, where the quality of communication about sexual matters at home is at best liable to be minimal, at worst totally inappropriate. Although the young people in the units are mostly teenagers, the emotional age of many is very far behind their chronological age, with enormous gaps in maturity and in the understanding of normal human relationships.

In residential care, each young person has a key worker, who becomes the person in the position of the trusted adult whilst a young person is in a unit. They may also confide in other practitioners regarding personal matters such as sexual health, for example, if their key worker is of the opposite sex and they do not feel comfortable discussing these issues with them. The young people are frequently resistant to and wary of strangers who may attempt to carry out work with them, and we found the most effective interventions were those done directly with the young people by their key workers or other residential care practitioners. Although in no way can this person be regarded as a parent substitute, if work is to be done to try to make up for some of the deficits in parenting in the early years (in terms of understanding relationships, answering questions regarding sexual behaviour, sexuality or sexual health) the keyworkers are best placed to support the young people.

We felt therefore that the RCHP had a role in ascertaining how confident the keyworkers were in advising, listening and guiding the young people on sexual health matters, and in asking them what support and training they needed to assume this role. It was not appropriate to single out sexual health as a separate issue, and we preferred to view it as part of a holistic approach to caring for the health of the young people. Therefore, the views of staff were sought in the staff training audit (see Part 2, page 35) as a part of an audit of knowledge and skill in dealing with issues about a wide range of health topics including physical health, child health and development, mental health and emotional wellbeing, support from health services and health promotion generally. The results provided the format of a training week on health issues (see Part 2, page 40), which addressed sexual health alongside general health issues, primary care, accessing services, mental health, and general health promotion within units.

Carers need to know where to seek advice, from time to time, for individual problems with young people. This need is much greater than that of most parents within the community; they are frequently coping with young people who have run away, had unprotected sex or who may have been sexually exploited or abused. It is very important to have a good knowledge of where to seek support, and how to access the agencies. At the start of the RCHP there were many calls for advice regarding sexual risk-taking for the young people. Support and the training week resulted in the staff being much more self sufficient in seeking appropriate services, but occasionally there is a need for easy access health advice for carers on an ongoing basis. The project nurses provided an invaluable source of telephone advice which could direct young people quickly towards services.

The young person: education and goals

Young people in general who have goals – whether they be to get a good job, earn a lot of money, go to college or university or travel – will be more careful to ensure that they do not put a halt to their immediate and longer-term plans by risking pregnancy.

In the House of Commons Select Committee report,[29] research on the education of looked after children showed that between 50% and 75% of care leavers had no academic qualifications. Only 12% to 19% of looked after and accommodated young people went on to further education, compared with 68% of the general population and non attendance and exclusions were common.

As lack of educational attainment is linked to perpetuation of the cycle of deprivation, and also to teenage pregnancy, there is an argument that the improvement of educational provision for looked after and accommodated children would bring about a significant improvement in their lifestyles and, thereby, in their health.

The young person: emotional wellbeing

Confidence and self esteem are central to good decision making and are essential for building healthy relationships. From the figures available in the comprehensive health assessment profile (see Part 2, page 18), it is clear that the young people here have a very high rate of emotional, behavioural and mental health problems (97% of those seen by the paediatrician had significant emotional, behavioural or mental health problems). Working with young people to lessen risk-taking behaviours, when they do not value themselves, can be counterproductive, thus the need for support from mental health services to work alongside good health promotion and education practices.

The young person: health education

Only 27% of young people covered by the RCHP, attended mainstream school. Therefore, as well as missing out on the parental guidance regarding sexual health that most young people get in the course of growing up, it cannot be assumed that this group will have accessed the school health education curriculum. In the past, health education packages delivered to YPCs has been largely crisis driven, and one of the main aims of the RCHP has been to move to a more planned model of health education for the young people.

Health education was delivered to the young people by various alternative means:

- Individually, according to the young person's needs, largely at health assessments
- Via carers, following sexual health training
- In group work, both with project nurses and by bringing in specialist sexual health promotion agencies

---

[29] House of Commons Select Committee on Health. Children Looked After by Local Authorities. (Second report). The Stationery Office. London 1998

Individual work

From the comprehensive health assessments, it was found that 31% of the young people admitted to having been sexually active (10% boys, 61% girls). Of those, 72% admitted to practising unsafe sex sometimes (48%) or always (24%). Only 18% were using contraception. If the young person was felt to be putting themselves at risk sexually, advice was given at the time of consultation by the paediatrician. If the young person was agreeable, this would be shared with their key worker, who could follow up the advice with further individual support.

Health promotion via carers

Most individual work with young people was carried out by the key workers, often with support from the nurse or paediatrician, or through the training programme. It could take several consultations before a young person would be trusting enough to discuss sensitive matters with someone other than the carer they knew and, although flexibility was applied, this generally proved to be the most acceptable way forward for young people.

Health promotion in group work and peer group issues

When the RCHP first started, advice from managers in units was that group work with the young people would not be a good idea, due to difficulties in managing behaviours, group dynamics or individual group members who might have particularly sensitive issues in their past experience. Care needed to be applied, bearing in mind that many of the young people will have been sexually abused, or may have experience of very abnormal and coercive sexual practices. However, as time went on, it became apparent that there was no one 'rule' regarding what suited all units. Whether or not to work with a group depended on the young people in question, whether they had been together for a reasonable length of time, what their needs were and so on. Two groups working with girls on a range of health issues in the secure units were very successfully evaluated, but a group working with boys in the same unit was completely unsuccessful, and had to be abandoned.

Consultation with the *Healthy Respect* partners was particularly valuable in setting up strategies to reach wider groups in other units. The nature of group work with outside agencies entailed the RCHP nurse setting up contact with a unit acting as the link between the specialist agency, staff and young people. This added a personal touch to the move to a more planned, less crisis-driven approach to sexual health promotion.

Media and information distribution networks

Healthy Respect, as part of its Lothian-wide programme, has set up information provision targeting those networks frequently accessed by young people – television, radio, events, educational settings, youth clubs, leisure settings and health venues such as surgeries and hospitals. A website has been set up and, as part of the educational plan for young people in residential care, information technology networks are being ensured in all residential units for access by young people and staff alike.

In conclusion

- Many young people in local authority residential care are unlikely to be able to access standard school health education programmes
- It is therefore necessary to look at alternative ways of delivering sexual health information and advice to them
- Factors which adversely affect sexual health for any population are very prevalent in this group, and are liable to impede any attempt at improvement unless they are robustly addressed
- Sexual health promotion needs to be looked at in the light of the whole life experience of the young people

- Sexual health needs to be viewed in the context of holistic health improvement
- Young people who do not trust adults need to be supported via those whom they do trust
- Carers need to be supported by health agencies to do this
- Delivering sexual health promotion to hard-to-reach, marginalised young people takes time and effort
- Better links with school nurses and education will help to ensure gaps in the curriculum are covered for young people who cannot access the standard curriculum
- Policy and practice must be developed with the specific needs of this group of young people in mind, and to be included in the regional sexual health strategy[30]
- If we do not change in this way, the young people who need sexual health advice the most will continue to get the least

Drug, alcohol and/or volatile substance use

In the completion of this chapter we would like to acknowledge these agencies who have been central to the needs assessment, development and implementation of services to young people and their carers in the Edinburgh, East Lothian and Midlothian areas.

- Fast Forward Positive Lifestyles Ltd[31]
- MELD (Mid and East Lothian Drugs)[32]
- HYPE (Help for Young People in Edinburgh)[33]

Introduction

From a recent Government White Paper,[34] the Scottish Executive has developed an enhanced drugs strategy for Scotland.[35]

Priorities identified in this strategy included:

- Provision of support for young people in vulnerable situations
- Improving the range and quality of drug services for young people, particularly under-16s
- Integrated services to assist early intervention with young misusers, particularly those with serious and sustained drug misuse problems
- Outreach work and early interventions
- Taking young people's views into account
- Improving preventive strategies

Local research at the Young People's Unit of the Child and Adolescent Mental Health Services (CAMHS) in Edinburgh in 1999[36] came forward with the following recommendations for young people and staff in the residential care setting:

---

[30] Patel-Kanwal H, *et al.* Let's Talk About Sex and Relationships: Developing and Reviewing Policy. National Children's Bureau. 1998.

[31] 4 Bernard Street, Edinburgh EH6 6PP. 0131-554 4300. www.fastforward.org.uk

[32] 4c Newmills Road, Dalkeith, Midlothian EH22 1DU. 0131-660 3566. www.meld-drugs.co.uk

[33] Simpson House, 52 Queen Street, Edinburgh EH2 3NS. 0131-466 4600. schype@mail.nch.org.uk

[34] Tackling Drugs to Build a Better Britain: The Government's Ten-Year Strategy for Tackling Drugs Misuse. Cm 3945. The Stationery Office, 1998.

[35] Tackling Drugs in Scotland: Action in Partnership. The Scottish Office. 1999.

[36] Robinson P, *et al.* Care Sick: The Physical and Mental Health Needs of Looked After and Accommodated Children and Adolescents in Residential Care: Public Health and Inequalities. Young People's Unit, Royal Edinburgh Hospital. Scottish Executive. 1999.

- Staff would appreciate more information about the effects of illicit drugs in order to offer accurate advice to young people
- Staff felt it would be helpful for young people to have access to the most contemporary information about health and drug issues
- Staff felt that social work policy regarding drug issues was at odds with other agencies
- Young people got different messages from different agencies which was confusing
- School attendance was poor in this group who often missed out on drug education programmes

The RCHP staff training audit identified training in drug, volatile substance and alcohol abuse as priority areas for further training (see Part 2, page 39).

Local government policy, in the form of the Edinburgh Drug Action Team's document [37] highlights the following priorities:

- Social work should develop a drugs policy and guidelines on harm reduction
- Guidelines need to be developed on the management of drug-related incidents for staff working in social work residential and day units with young people
- Protocols need to be developed for joint working with specialist drug agencies
- Social work should continue to incorporate substance misuse training with the programme for staff working with young people in a range of care settings

The RCHP, in its early development, made links with as many agencies working with looked after and accommodated children and young people as possible (see Part 1, page 4). Where health initiatives were successfully under way, the RCHP met with other professionals involved to establish whether or not we had a role in the delivery of services so avoiding duplication of effort and resulting confusion for units and young people.

The geographical area served by the RCHP was fortunate in having some excellent initiatives under way for young people regarding drug, alcohol and volatile substance use, both in terms of education for young people and carers, and individual counselling and support for the young people. The RCHP therefore did not become directly involved in the provision of services, but worked closely with the other providers to meet the needs of the young people and their carers. A representative of one of the agencies became a member of the RCHP Advisory Group.

Three main agencies are involved. Fast Forward, a drug education programme supported by BBC Children In Need, has been assessing the drug education needs of vulnerable young people in the Edinburgh area and has been delivering education programmes to young people and those who work with them. MELD employs workers who carry out training for foster carers, day carers and parents and provides counselling and support work for young people. HYPE, managed by NCH Scotland and working in partnership with the City of Edinburgh Council, provides free confidential counselling and support work for young people aged 18 and under within Edinburgh who have difficulties related to their use of drugs, alcohol and/or volatile substances. Family support and counselling is also offered if the young person is agreeable. There are strong links with Lothian Primary Care Trust's Drug Problems Service (CDPS), and an agreement is in place that HYPE will assess all young people aged 17 and under who are referred to CDPS, thus acknowledging the special needs of this group.

---

[37] A Drugs Strategy for the City of Edinburgh 1999-2000. City of Edinburgh Council, Lothian Health, Lothian & Borders Police, Coalition of Drug Agencies, HM Prison Edinburgh. City of Edinburgh Council 1999.

During the time of the RCHP, these services have been developing and expanding in parallel, and have been the main source of support and advice on drug, alcohol and volatile substance use for the young people and their carers.

A major assessment of the drug education needs of vulnerable young people in Edinburgh, carried out by Fast Forward between July and December 2000[38] found that young people 'looked after and accommodated' in Edinburgh had received little or no drug education at school, probably as a result of poor or erratic school attendance. The young people were keen to discuss their thoughts and feelings on drug-related issues, and felt that adults did not spend enough time discussing this with them.

Vulnerable young people who were looked after and accommodated required information on drugs to come from an unbiased and credible source, preferably outwith the residential unit, and without unit staff present. Time was needed to get to know the young people, and those delivering the education preferably included young people with personal experience of drugs.

Staff who cared for vulnerable young people often felt that the young people knew more about drugs than they did, and were concerned about mixed messages on drugs that young people were receiving from staff. Both drug and alcohol awareness training, and support on these issues for staff, were felt to be required.

Fast Forward has subsequently had contact with all the YPCs, and has run 197 substance awareness sessions to 3466 young people in a variety of settings, among them YPCs, youth projects, programmes for young unemployed people, support agencies for homeless young people and young offenders. Twenty-one full day training courses on substance awareness have been delivered to 298 professionals who provide care and support to vulnerable young people within Lothian.

The service provided by HYPE has been expanded and developed over the past year to employ three new full-time residential care project staff who will focus on providing outreach support services for young people in residential care, foster care and throughcare. They will also work with social workers, parents, carers and schools, as required, to help the young people. The development will be rigorously evaluated over the coming years to ensure appropriate service development.

As the RCHP draws to a close, provision of these services for one of the major developments to underpin ongoing support for young people and staff, has been ensured – another part of a large multi-agency approach to supporting young people who are looked after and accommodated. The looked after children health team look forward to continuing to work with these agencies for the improvement of the health and wellbeing of the young people.

Dental health

Dental caries and periodontal disease may not be life-threatening but can cause a lot of unnecessary pain, discomfort and social embarrassment. Oral neglect is a symptom of a deeper lack of regard for personal health, which is manifested in so many other elements of the Scottish lifestyle. We owe it to ourselves to change these attitudes and to enjoy the benefits from a fitter and healthier nation.[39][40]

---

38 Assessment of the Drug Education Needs of Vulnerable Young People in Edinburgh. Fast Forward Positive Lifestyles Ltd. Feb 2001.

39 Scotland's Health: A Challenge To Us All: A Policy Statement. The Scottish Office. HMSO. 1992.

40 Oral Health Strategy for Scotland. The Scottish Office, 1995.

Background

The Scottish Health Boards' Dental Epidemiological Programme report[41] of a survey of 14-year-old children in 1998/9 identified a strong association between deprivation and dental decay; almost four times as many children in the least-deprived category are 'free' of caries compared with their more unfortunate contemporaries in the most deprived category. There is also an uneven distribution of dental decay, with small groups having very high levels of decay.

Lothian Oral Health Strategy Implementation Group[42] priority targets include all children in areas of deprivation, and their parents and carers. Recommendations for a way forward include healthy eating guidelines, a multi-agency approach to promote oral health, working with the community dental service to offer dental care in areas of poor uptake, and generally incorporating oral health promotion into corporate planning. Diet, dental registration with regular attendance and personal oral hygiene are all identified as crucial family roles. For young people in residential care, these roles fall upon carers, in terms of a corporate parenting role and the development of the health promoting unit. The maximum period between oral examinations for everyone, irrespective of age or dental condition, should be one year,[43] but children may need to be seen more frequently, as may those at risk of oral disease through smoking, medical, physical or social factors.

In the 12 months leading up to the start of the RCHP, one of the project nurses secured funding to work from a primary care base in two residential units in south-east Edinburgh to address the health needs of the young people looked after and accommodated there.[44] Of the 13 young people in the two units, only one (7.7%) had seen a dentist within the preceding year. By the end of this health empowerment project, 10 of the young people (77%) had attended the dentist, some taking up to six visits to complete their treatment. A high level of commitment was needed to achieve these results, with time, patience and understanding of the needs of this group. To have completed treatment gave the young people a sense of achievement. The concept was not about a young person having to leave a dentist they attended but putting a service in place for each home to use and building effective working relationships with the community dental service for when a young person had no dentist.

The Residential Care Health Project (RCHP)

After the start of the RCHP it became obvious that there was a problem with dental care in other units throughout the region, and that it would be helpful to use lessons learned in the Health Empowerment Project to implement a system for all units in the area of the RCHP. Consultations therefore took place with the Community Dental Service (CDS) to develop the work into a Lothian-wide service for residential care. The work of raising awareness of oral health issues started from the outset of the project, having been highlighted in the Health Empowerment Project, and continued throughout, culminating in National Smile Week in May 2002.

The aims of the dental project were:

- To link each residential unit with their nearest community dentist
- To establish a Lothian-wide service
- To organise dental health promotion packs for each young person

---

[41] Pitts NB, *et al.* Report of the 1998/99 Scottish Health Board's Dental Epidemiological Programme Survey of 14 Year Old Children. University of Dundee Dental Health Services Research Unit, 1999.

[42] Lothian Local Health Plan 2002. Lothian NHS Board, 2002.

[43] The Scientific Basis of Dental Health Education: A Policy Document (revised fourth edition). Health Development Agency, 2001.

[44] Sinclair L. Health Empowerment Project. Lothian Primary Care Trust. 2000 (unpublished).

- To roll out the service simultaneously to all units during National Smile Week (May 2002)
- To inform dental colleagues of the particular needs of this group of young people through meetings and seminars
- To incorporate oral health into a holistic view of health promotion and care for young people
- To train carers in aspects of dental care

Method

Units which were already working with a local dentist were encouraged to continue with that service, but to use the CDS as an additional support. Contact was made with the oral health promotion worker from the CDS, whose team planned to visit each unit. This aimed to promote healthy diet, sensible use of preventive measures, and access to dental treatment and oral health care when required.[45] Packs for each young person – including a toothbrush, toothpaste, disclosing tablets and a quiz – were jointly funded between RCHP, Community Dental Services and the health promotion department of the Health Board. An information booklet was put together specifically for the use of care workers and young people.

During National Smile Week, the RCHP nurses delivered the packs and booklets to each home. The senior community dentist wrote to all unit managers introducing the service and giving details of their local community dentist. New initiatives to monitor the health needs of looked after children from the moment they enter the care system ensure that the need for dental health care is identified and highlighted at an early stage.

Outcome

In June 2002 an audit of all young people in units was carried out and 11 units, with 71 young people resident, responded. 64.7% of the young people had been seen by a dentist within the past year. Attendance at the dentist varied from 100% in two of the units to 0% in one, suggesting that, with commitment, good dental attendance can be achieved. Training for staff and the health promoting presence of the RCHP has raised awareness of all aspects of oral health and dental care to the benefit of young people in the units.

Immunisations

Immunisation is the most effective way to protect young people against many serious infections. It is largely because of routine immunisation programmes that infectious diseases including diphtheria, tuberculosis and measles are rarely heard of in Scotland these days. *Of the children and young people seen by the Residential Care Health Project paediatrician, 71% had incomplete courses of immunisation* (see Part 2, page 26).

One of the targets of the project was therefore to improve the uptake of immunisations by children and young people in residential care. We hoped to achieve this by:

- Providing information to carers on immunisation and immunisation services
- Raising awareness of service providers to the barriers to uptake which exist for this group

---

[45] Lothian Oral Health Strategy. Lothian NHS Board, 1998.

- Improving access to services
- Introducing flexibility to services
- Improving recording systems to assist care planning with respect to immunisations, and as required by the 'Looking After Children' materials

What did we do?

A nurse led task group was formed, with representation from the central immunisation recall service, school nursing and the BCG service, to get a clear understanding of central recording systems and mainstream service delivery. Further consultations took place with public health medicine colleagues regarding BCG immunisation. The main providers of immunisations are primary care (usually health visitors or practice nurses) and school health services, and it was evident from the figures that the mainstream services were not meeting the needs of a mobile population who tend to be irregular school attenders.

In the geographical area of the RCHP, school health immunisation programmes consist of planned sessions which those with poor school attendance are likely to miss. We decided to recommend that young people were taken to the GP for immunisations which were overdue, with the exception of BCG. The school health service programme offers BCG to children aged 14, and there is also a central service operating from a chest clinic for high-risk groups only. On further discussion it was felt that the central service was not the appropriate one to meet the needs of the client group. Discussions ensued with the school nurse manager, school nurse immunisation coordinator and appropriate representatives of the education department, and agreement was reached that young people who were due or had missed BCG immunisation could attend a scheduled programme in any school. No particular problems were anticipated, as the likely numbers involved were 15 to 20 per year. As a result of this arrangement, between March 2002 and June 2002 ten young people who had missed BCG had successfully been immunised with the cooperation of the school nurses and the education department.

The initial notes audit showed that only 9% of young people in residential care at that time had details of immunisations in their files. As part of the exit plan for the RCHP, a statement of immunisation status is provided for all children on becoming accommodated, with guidance on outstanding immunisations.

A guidance pack was also provided for each unit containing general information on immunisations, a check list of questions on health status likely to be asked at the time of immunising, contact numbers of school nurses and a schedule of BCG sessions. A flow chart was added to direct action when the immunisation status of young people was known. The guidance packs, along with statements for individual young people, were distributed to the units via the health link workers.

Through these methods, awareness of the immunisation needs of this group has been raised in health and social work agencies. Unit staff have not reported any difficulties in arranging immunisations at GP surgeries. As we move towards a system where more detailed background information on young people can be provided for carers at entry to the care system this will, hopefully, become an area where uptake of preventive health care can approach and equal that of children and young people living at home with their parents.

Secure units

Secure accommodation is a small but necessary part of the overall network of services for children,[46] and is included in the children's services plans. A child may be placed in secure accommodation under a supervision requirement made by a children's hearing. He or she may also be placed in secure accommodation by the court in certain circumstances under parts V and X1 of the Criminal Procedure (Scotland) Act 1995.[47] In other situations the chief social work officer can authorise a placement in secure accommodation with the agreement of the person in charge of the establishment.

Children being placed in secure accommodation have been found to be a significant danger to themselves or to others in the community. This is a serious intervention, designed to rehabilitate and, where necessary, to protect the public. There are many regulations around the welfare, quality of care, education and rights of the children. The Act acknowledges that this group of young people is more likely to have special health problems caused by adverse experiences and frequent changes of placement and includes guidance regarding medical examination, health records, access to mental health provision and attention to concerns regarding drug, alcohol or substance abuse.

In Edinburgh there are two secure units, St Katharine's and Howdenhall, which provide a facility for both boys and girls. In the year May 2000-May 2001, Howdenhall (capacity five secure beds) had 20 admissions and 20 discharges, and St Katharine's (capacity seven secure beds) had 19 admissions and 23 discharges. The average stay was 89 days in Howdenhall and 70 days in St Katharine's and the ages ranged from 11 to 15 years. Both secure units also have 'Close Support' beds.

The most common reasons for care were young people placing themselves at risk and absconding from home or care.

When a young person is admitted to a secure unit, they are in a safe environment with decreased levels of environmental distraction. The admission period represents the ideal time for a full and comprehensive assessment, followed by intensive therapeutic work. The goal of the RCHP has been to move towards the creation of a *gold standard of integrated health care* for Edinburgh's secure units using a truly multidisciplinary approach at policy, management and operational levels, involving the following agencies:

- Social work management and residential care staff
- Primary care
- Community child health
- Mental health
- Education

Social work and care staff

The RCHP has audited the training needs of staff (see Part 2, page 35) and initiated a comprehensive health training programme. Links made at managerial level have aimed at continuing this. Health promotion has been forwarded directly with young people and staff, and by bringing in other agencies involved in health promotion for young people. A health resource pack (see Part 3, page 71) is being developed in collaboration with social work and the Health Education Board for Scotland (HEBS) – now NHS Health Scotland. Staff have been encouraged to develop 'in house' management of minor ailments through the use of a family health care book, in the context of more appropriate use of health services in general.

---

[46] Children (Scotland) Act 1995: Regulations and Guidance. Social Work Services Group, Scottish Office. The Stationery Office. 1997. 92-105.

[47] Criminal Procedure (Scotland) Act 1995. The Stationery Office. 1995.

Gold standard model

- To develop the model of the health promoting unit
- To enable other agencies to offer direct work (1:1 or group) with these children (including alcohol, drug and substance use counselling and education, sexual health education)
- Encourage and welcome other agencies to offer training and support to staff
- Ensure that every unit has a health resource pack which is regularly maintained
- Ongoing social work-funded programme of health training based on evaluated training and interventions

Primary care

Prior to the RCHP, obtaining primary care services for secured children was problematic: no practice was formally contracted to provide primary care services for young people in the units. The very reasons for young people being in a secure unit immediately produce barriers to accessing primary care services as currently structured. Young people are there largely because they are a risk to themselves or others. Many are liable to use any opportunity to abscond; some are the subject of secure orders imposed by courts and may not go out other than under police escort; hardly appropriate for surgery consultations.

The young people tend to start out in secure units without their freedom and, as their management progresses, they will move to 'close support' accommodation where they have a degree of freedom and may attend appointments. As far as possible, 'normalisation' is the aim in terms of health care provision. However, there are occasions when primary care services will be required for a young person in a secure unit who is feeling unwell and unable to attend the practice. This needs to be acknowledged.

One of the recommendations in the 2001 HMI inspection of care arrangements and education at the secure units in Edinburgh was that *'The provision of adequate emergency primary care cover should be formalised within the Residential Care Health Project'*.[48]

Early on in the project, a GP researcher was appointed to look at the unique difficulties and needs of young people in the residential care system in terms of accessing primary care, and also the problems encountered by primary care in delivering services to residential care, in particular the secure units. Excellent support was forthcoming from primary care management and eventually, through Personal Medical Services (PMS) funding, a practice has been identified whereby both secure units can be affiliated to one GP practice base, with a mutually agreed contract. This arrangement has provided an opportunity for social work and community child health to work closely with one practice, and to examine critically the often extreme medical dilemmas which young people in secure units can present. The management of these primary care based medical crises often goes much further than health. Specialist advice and expertise is requested, health care plans are developed prior to entry into the secure unit, or background information is provided by community child health and social work which is essential to support the GPs in their work.

---

[48] Inspection of Care Arrangements and Education in: Secure Units Howdenhall and St Katharine's Centres. City of Edinburgh Council: Joint Report by Social Work Services Inspectorate and HM Inspectorate of Education. Scottish Executive. 2001.

Gold standard model

- Both units affiliated to one single GP practice base, with a mutually agreed contract, reducing problems for both patients and staff in accessing primary care, and facilitating improved liaison between young people, staff, primary care, community child health and other agencies

- A specifically designed registration form is completed within 24 hours of admission. This details registration data for the young person as well as identifying any immediate medical needs such as infestation or potential drug withdrawal

- If the young person has been registered with a different local practice, a special form is sent to this registered GP inquiring if they wish to continue to provide medical services during the stay in the secure unit. This ensures that the care workers are completely clear about which practice to contact for each young person

- GP medical files are fast-tracked via Practitioner Services Division

- The traditional Into-Care Medicals have been replaced by a comprehensive health assessment iniated by the nurse for looked after children

- The practice nurse or GP follows up health needs identified and within a primary care remit

- To facilitate easy access to the practice, a protected daily appointment is allocated to these young people, coinciding with care workers shift overlap at 3 pm; this allows the unit to organise in advance for a care worker to accompany the young person to the surgery. The appointments are for both acute and follow-up consultations, mainly with the same doctor, thus promoting continuity of care and building an ongoing relationship

- When particular difficulties in management have arisen, multi-disciplinary significant event analyses have been important in developing health care policy within the secure units

Community child health

The results of the RCHP audit of comprehensive health assessments for young people in the secure units has shown the high level of unmet health needs and poor prior health information for this group of children.

With the recent appointment of a nurse for looked after children, and community child health taking ownership of the management of health tracking for looked after children and young people as an integral part of the service, there will be a continuing communication link, the opportunity of triage and contact with other agencies to support the young people.

Gold standard model

- Community child health will provide initial health assessments for all children entering the care system as part of the drive to improve the health of looked after children

- Carer held health records will be provided for each child

- The community child health department has a commitment to provide comprehensive health assessments to all young people entering secure units, identifying areas of need and making recommendations for health management

- RCHP protocol followed for immunisations (Part 5, page 88)

- Community Child Health will provide the affiliated GP practice with any information gathered in the course of the assessment, and will act as a source of reference for social work and primary care staff

Mental health

The 2001 joint report of the inspection of care arrangements and education at the Edinburgh Secure Units[49] recommends that a mental health needs assessment should be completed in both centres with active consideration given to the implications for services, their integration in the existing range of provision and management arrangements.

The results of the audit of the RCHP comprehensive health assessments (see Part 2, page 18) has revealed, not unexpectedly, an extremely high prevalence of emotional, behavioural and mental health problems in these children. These figures have supported social work, education and health in Edinburgh in a successful bid for 'Changing Children's Services' monies for a dedicated mental health service for children and young people who are looked after and accommodated, particularly those in residential care. They have also raised awareness within the other local authorities of the need for mental health supports for looked after children within developing frameworks. One area which will receive particular attention will be the assessment of need in the secure units. The following is the RCHP's view of the necessary supports.

Gold standard model

- Easy access to prompt consultation services, emergency services, and adolescent forensic psychiatric services as required
- All children in secure units to have a mental health assessment as part of the placement process
- Strong links with child and adolescent mental health services
- Immediate and direct therapeutic work available from the time of placement
- Ongoing training for staff about management of mental health issues

Education

The RCHP audit of Comprehensive Health Assessments (see Part 2, page 12) indicates that there is a significant number of children with learning difficulties, associated dyspraxia, and problems of attention and concentration which would impair learning. Surprisingly, the inspection at Howdenhall and St Katharine's Secure Units 2000-2001 stated that there were no children with records of need.

Level of education has a close correlation with adult health and teenage pregnancy. It is also one of the most significant factors perpetuating the cycle of deprivation. The following is the RCHP view of necessary interventions:

Gold standard model

- A full cognitive and educational assessment of all young people entering the secure facility, contributing to their care plan and individual education plan, thereby influencing the choice of their future educational resource
- Training for staff on appropriate approaches to the identification and care of young people with special educational needs

Concluding summary

While a young person is secured, the gold standard model comprises the undertaking of a full and comprehensive health assessment including, specifically, a mental health assessment. There would be joint working involving all health agencies, particularly primary care, community child health and child and adolescent mental health services. The health services would link fully with social work and education services to provide a full and informed base for a management and therapy plan.

---

[49] Inspection of Care Arrangements and Education in: Secure Units Howdenhall and St Katharine's Centres. City of Edinburgh Council: Joint Report by Social Work Services Inspectorate and HM Inspectorate of Education. Scottish Executive. 2001.

Health resource pack

As a project team we became a source of support and advice for our social work colleagues but, in the context of a time-limited project, we were mindful of the need for initiatives to be sustainable in our absence. It was therefore proposed that we develop a health resource pack containing dedicated health information and advice for the carers of looked after children. Before progressing, we first had to consider the support for such an initiative.

Policy and research support for a health resource pack

As previously highlighted, looked after and accommodated children and young people suffer from dire health inequalities. The influencing factors are many and complex, however, of great significance is their lack of access to relevant health education and health promotion advice, and their poor access to appropriate health care services. *Working Together for a Healthier Scotland*[50] supports a targeted approach to tackling health inequalities and highlights child health as a priority. Also, the *National Care Standards*[51] indicate that care staff must be able to offer children and young people guidance on healthy lifestyles and on how to access required health care services. As such, current policy and research supports the development of targeted health advice for carers of looked after children.

Local support for a health resource pack

Local evidence confirmed the need for a health resource pack. The comprehensive health training needs analysis (see Part 2, page 35), carried out in the early stages of the project, indicated that residential care workers did not receive adequate health training and support. Workers concurred that they lacked the knowledge and skills necessary to deal with health issues effectively and confirmed that they were not fully aware of available health care services. Working alongside our social work colleagues, we recognised that they were ideally placed to advise young people on their health, and to deliver health promotion messages. However, working within highly pressurised environments, carers were often limited to a crisis-led approach, only being able to react to health issues as they emerged. Staff who attended health training week organised by the RCHP felt that there was a lack of health resources specifically for looked after and accommodated young people, and welcomed the development of this dedicated health resource pack.

Key aims of the health resource pack

Our key aim was to work with social work colleagues to produce an accessible health resource pack suitable for use by both foster carers and residential care workers. We aimed to illustrate the broad nature of health and provide specific health information that would enable carers to meet the particular needs of looked after children. We also hoped to increase carers' awareness of available health care services in an effort to promote a more equitable access to services by this marginalised group. We wanted the health resource pack to help carers develop their skills and confidence in relation to the delivery of health promotion/health education messages. In broad terms, we wanted the health resource pack to make health a priority issue, and provide ongoing support and encouragement for both foster carers and residential care workers to take a more proactive approach towards health care issues.

---

[50] Working Together for a Healthier Scotland. Scottish Executive. 1998.

[51] National Care Standards: Care Homes for Children and Young People. Scottish Executive. 2002.

Development of the health resource pack

The initial developments took place during the six-month period from February to July 2002. Having established that carers would value this resource, a RCHP task group and a wider development group were convened. Joint funding was agreed with all of the Lothian social work departments, the Health Education Board for Scotland, *Healthy Respect* and the RCHP contributing. The development group comprised staff members from the RCHP team, five residential care units, HEBS and *Healthy Respect* (NHS Lothian) and was therefore representative of both Health and Social Work. Several meetings of the development group led to the design of a comprehensive consultation document circulated to approximately 120 foster carers and residential care workers. Analysis of 45 completed questionnaires – 31 from residential care workers and 14 from foster carers, making a 38% response rate – allowed the RCHP task group to write a detailed brief and to commission writers to undertake the work.

Future development

Development of the resource pack, including its writing, launch and evaluation, is being overseen by the development group and the RCHP advisory group. We anticipate that the pack will be available for public launch around the end of 2003. It is hoped that this resource, with minor local adaptations, will be able to support carers on the wider national scale.

Summary

We believe that the completed health resource pack will provide continued support for foster carers and residential care workers. It will contain specific health information to help them better meet the particular health needs of looked after children and young people, and also increase their skills and confidence in dealing with the many complex health issues which arise. We also anticipate that the pack will increase carers' awareness of available health care services, and so encourage more frequent and appropriate use.

Although it was time-consuming to plan and organise multi-agency meetings, particularly with so many group members working through changing shift patterns, the joint working process used to develop the pack will be central to its success. This method of working ensures better communication between different professional groups, and ensures a clearer understanding of the key issues affecting those concerned. The joint working method guarantees the relevance of the pack and this, in turn, will ensure that it is a well-used resource.

Part 4 Developing Strategies for Sustainability

Developing strategies within the health sector

Working to improve health care for young people looked after and accommodated in local authority residential care requires all concerned to take a considered look at the roles and responsibilities of those who care for them, whether in Health, Social Work, Education or the voluntary agencies. As the ultimate responsibility for the young person's wellbeing and safety rests with the Social Work department, any new health initiatives or changes in practice must be done in partnership with the local authority. If changes which may affect working practice need to be made in the way we deliver health services, the reasons must be clearly demonstrated. Moves towards change have to be negotiated and agreed at all levels for sustainable progress to be made. A project involving health service delivery from many different sources, such as this, brings with it a major strategic role in developing and linking services *within* and *between* agencies.

From past research, and from the information gathered in the course of the RCHP, it is clear that the primary cause of the poor health outcomes for this group of young people is not the state of a child's health on the day they enter the care system. It is rather the history of unmet health need prior to becoming accommodated, the missed preventive health measures, appointments and health promotion opportunities, subtle developmental difficulties, and significant mental health and emotional behavioural problems. These are compounded by the lack of our current health care systems to adapt to the needs of a mobile population, by difficulties of tracking children and young people, and of communication between and within agencies. These issues can only be addressed by a coordinated approach to tracking and intervention, in which all areas of health service provision have a role to play.

Our experiences highlighted the need for a single system within health to take ownership of the entire process *from the time of entry into the care system*, to collate information, to track and monitor health care, and to provide easy access to simple advice on where to find help about a range of health issues. We have also highlighted the need for flexibility in health care delivery services, and particularly the need for truly interagency working practice which is supported at all levels, from service delivery to senior management. These basic principles underpin the changes which have been put in place to provide sustainable change in health care for the children and young people, and constitute the essence of the exit plan of the RCHP.

Residential Care Health Project exit plan

The exit plan of the RCHP involves every area in which we have worked since the start of the project. From the outset of this initiative, the prime aim has been to work towards sustainable change. Some of this has happened by radically changing the way in which services are delivered, without the need for additional funding. When working in an area of such profound disadvantage and inequality, however, it is not surprising that some previously neglected areas of health care have been exposed which will require ongoing and extensive support in the future. The most obvious of these are addressing the children's needs from the time of entry into the care system, and the enormous unmet need for mental health support and care.

Throughout the RCHP there has been increasing awareness at Scottish Executive and Health Board level of the huge health needs of looked after children, so proposals for implementing improvements are being considered as priorities. We have been fortunate in having the opportunity to take a holistic look at the entire health system, and at how it interacts with social services and education. We have concluded that the way in which health supports for looked after and accommodated children have been set up is outmoded in today's health service, with inappropriate use of services which is both wasteful of resources and does not meet the needs of the children. We also cannot overstate the vital interdependence between all branches of health services, social services and education to improve the health prospects for these young people: no one agency alone can change the situation in a sustainable way.

There follows a summary of actions which have been taken – or which are in the process of development – to maintain the improvements initiated in the past years.

The main actions include:

Health service provision

- *One agency, community child health, taking ownership* of the management and follow-up of the health care of looked after and accommodated children and young people
- *Development of a system based on a nursing infrastructure*, with clearly accessible links to all levels of support in other health agencies
- *The permanent appointment of a nurse for looked after children*, with further development under way
- Looked after children nurse and community child health working closely with social services to assess need and provide the information necessary to care safely for the children *at the time of entry into the care system – residential care AND foster care*
- *Redesign of initial health assessments* for looked after children
- *Use of carer held health records*
- *Close liaison* with carers and with colleagues in *primary care, school health, mental health and specialist services* to make appropriate use of available services
- *Local lead paediatrician and lead nurse for looked after children working together* to ensure standards are achieved and maintained
- *Closer links between residential units and allied GP practices*
- The setting up of systems to ensure that *health records are fast-tracked* to new general practitioners after moves of care
- Ensuring that *all children are registered with a local GP* unless they are within close reach of their previous GP
- Ensuring that *all children are considered for full registration with a local GP if a placement lasts for three months*
- *The recognition of the need for shared care between community child health, primary care and the secure units for the management of the health of young people in secure units*
- Closer links between *community dental services* and residential units
- Closer links between *community pharmacists* and residential units
- The paediatrician and nurse for looked after children becoming an essential part of a *multi-agency team to improve the health and wellbeing of looked after children*
- Working with mental health colleagues towards *dedicated mental health services for looked after children*

- Continuing to work with *specialist health promotion agencies to target vulnerable children and young people*
- *Working with Healthy Respect to develop sexual health support services targeting vulnerable young people*
- The ongoing development of a *national special interest nurses' group for looked after children*

Social services

- Continuing to be part of a *multidisciplinary strategy group for looked after children*
- Continuing to work with social work management to *plan ongoing health improvements and developments*
- *Continuing multi-agency residential care health steering group* to ensure standards maintained
- *Developing the role of the health link worker* in residential units to implement health and health promotion developments
- *Health link worker role* is becoming an integral part of residential care practitioner *employee development*
- *Health training for care staff at all levels* is ongoing and becoming incorporated into social work training for carers, supported by designated health practitioners for looked after children

Education

- *Continuing to work in partnership with colleagues in education* to ensure that full, multi-agency assessment of needs for looked after children is carried out, including assessment of educational needs
- *Recognition by the health team of the effects of poor educational attainment and failure on the eventual outcomes for young people in terms of social functioning, mental health and wellbeing, and escaping from the cycle of deprivation*

Health service provision

We set out to refocus ownership and responsibility for the coordination of health care for the children and young people. Our aim was to support those working in the units, to explain about various health service providers and the range of services available within primary care, community child health and hospital, specialist and voluntary sectors.

We wanted to set up a system whereby each young person would have a reliable medical history and health record, and access to primary care, community child health and specialist services which equalled that of young people who were not looked after and accommodated. Also, we aimed to provide background information to support general practitioners, and others working with the young people, to carry out their role more effectively.

Young people, on arrival at a unit, may bring with them some health issues which are completely unfamiliar to those caring for them. General practitioners are also likely to have to deal with young people with complex health needs, armed with little or no background health information. We recognised that one priority was to work with primary care colleagues to ensure that health information is shared throughout the different services, and to ensure that responsibilities for various aspects of care lie with the most appropriate providers.

To combat the effect of working in isolation with young people, we saw the need for a central dedicated health professional to follow their progress, and to support social work staff and carers, particularly, in sharing information between branches of the health services. This would link to the vital improvement in tracking and information gathering central to any evolving service. To that end, administration of the whole system needs a dedicated process to ensure that this is achieved, requiring good administrative and information technology skills as well as those of health practitioners.

Strategy for community child health

Practice is variable throughout the country regarding provision of health services for looked after children. In the area of the RCHP (Edinburgh, East Lothian and Midlothian), health assessments of looked after children were previously performed almost exclusively in the primary care sector through a statutory mechanism known as the Reception into Care (RIC) medical. This examination informs largely on the physical health of the young person at the time of entry to the care system, and tended to be unhelpful in promoting better health. Without a more supported system, there is a tendency to view the 'medical' as part of an administrative process, a form to be completed, rather than using it as a tool to underpin health improvements.

There has, during the period of the RCHP, been a radical redirection of health care services for all looked after children, not just those within the residential care sector. Health Improvement Programme monies from the health board provided a timely opportunity, on a *permanent* basis, to take ownership of the health care process throughout Lothian. The system which has been set up in consultation with colleagues in social work and the various health support agencies, is built around the provision of *nursing and clerical support for looked after children*. Set within the community child health department, it displays an acceptance that the health of vulnerable children, and looked after children in particular, is a key community child health role.

This has enabled a radical *redesign of the initial health assessment for looked after children* (RIC medical). Social services ensure that the child becoming accommodated is known to the community child health service from the outset, enabling staff to gather all available information from many and varied health systems, to present to the health professional when the child is seen for an initial health assessment. This makes for a much more meaningful assessment and provides immediate access to a health care professional at this stage by telephone, if required, for advice. With a central nurse tracking and advisory service, health has taken ownership of ensuring that any health problems identified are understood and acted upon appropriately. Links to the community child health department ensure that further advice and more in-depth assessment are available for those children who need it, with the minimum delay. An added advantage is that, even for young people who refuse a medical examination, valuable information regarding their past history and health needs can still be gathered as they are frequently willing to have a health interview with the nurse. Given the nature of the identified health problems of these young people, very little is liable to be identified in a physical examination which cannot be identified in triage by an experienced nurse.

There is an acceptance that all of the health information required to care adequately for a child may take a few weeks to collate, but that the end product will be of much more value to the child and carer than a brief 'one off' report. The added advantage is that the information is then available for health professionals who need it, making the task of general practitioners and hospital practitioners dealing with these children more straightforward. The use of a carer-held record[1] documents the health profile and needs of the child in a user-friendly way for the child and their carer. Use of this model should lead to a coordinated approach to health care for the children and young people which will result in better and more meaningful uptake of services. We are finding that the children and young people being assessed, when first becoming accommodated, generally have much less entrenched problems which are more straightforward to address than those which were identified later during the RCHP. Hopefully, with this additional support, services will be identified earlier for young people developing more complex difficulties.

---

[1] Health Record. British Agencies for Adoption & Fostering.

In Scotland, unlike the rest of the United Kingdom, there is no requirement for periodic health assessments during the placement. The Children (Scotland) Act 1995 Regulations and Guidance[2] decrees that local authorities should decide, in consultation with local child health services, in which circumstances and how regularly it would be beneficial for such children to have health assessments. This system of ownership and tracking of health care management lends itself ideally to this concept, with reviews being built in at the most appropriate intervals, according to need.

The health problems identified by the paediatrician on the project were often known about by health professionals years before the young people were seen in the units but, due to frequent moves of placement, tracking and communication, this information was not passed on to the social work department. Early identification and easily available advice should improve the situation for all children and young people who are accommodated, whether in foster care or in residential care.

Strategy for primary care
MODEL FOR AN ALLIED PRIMARY HEALTH CARE TEAM

Primary care liaison was prioritised early in the project by the appointment of a GP with research experience onto the RCHP team through the support of senior management within the local primary care trust. By drawing on a working knowledge of general practice, the project could clarify the realities and challenges that this particular group of young people bring to the processes of primary health care provision.

In contrast to the community child health service, no one department can represent all of primary care. For good reason, the shape of local primary care services remains largely the remit of local GP surgeries and, in particular, with the GPs themselves. This system has allowed providers to build a sound and intimate picture of practice populations in order to build a local service sensitive to local needs.

The last decade has seen new cooperative ways of working enhance this system. Local Health Care Co-operatives (LHCCs) have brought together groups of primary health care teams to enable more streamlined approaches, where this has been appropriate. Managerial and developmental support for the LHCCs in the area served by the RCHP is provided by the Lothian Primary Health Care Trust.

At the start of the project, all residential units in the geographical area covered already had one identified GP practice which they consulted for the young people in their care (if it was not possible for the young person to remain with their original GP, for reasons, usually, of distance). In the course of the RCHP a model for *enhancing the links with the allied primary health care teams* developed, built on existing good practice, and formed the basis of a more meaningful link between residential units and their local GP surgery. The model was shared with local primary care teams in the context of all the developments currently being brought forward for looked after children and young people in the area. This has resulted in an improved understanding of ways of working for all carers and providers and, ultimately, we hope it will improve access to, and provision of, health care for the young people themselves.

Early on in the life of the RCHP, it was identified that a *health link worker* within each unit would be an invaluable resource as main contact. They would also have responsibility for developing health initiatives in conjunction with the health services. These members of the care staff have been encouraged to develop closer working relationships with the GP, practice manager and a nurse from the primary health care team. Units which already had strong relationships with their local practices tended to be those where there was a GP or nurse in the practice with a particular interest in the welfare of this group.

---

[2] Children (Scotland) Act 1995: Regulations and Guidance. Social Work Services Group, Scottish Office. The Stationery Office. 1997. 92-105.

The allied primary health care team model proposes a refocusing of work in six main areas: registration, health assessment, casenotes and continuity, health promotion, community dental services and community pharmacy services.

REGISTRATION

Registration with the local GP practice is currently problematic as it is perceived that young people move on after very short periods in residential units. In reality, care practitioners are often able to gauge the longevity of stay within a few days and are required to provide a placement decision within 12 weeks. The average length of stay is nine months but the range of stay may extend to more than three years.

Temporary Registration (TR) at a practice provides a fee for service payment. Unfortunately TR status does not invoke the mechanisms of continuity of care that come with full registration. This includes a central call for casenotes and an invitation to attend for a registration medical; the latter covers a review of immunisation status and a health promotion check, usually performed by the practice nurse.

Our model proposes that young people in the local residential units are fully registered at three months; this is coincident with the period in which placement in the unit, and therefore within the local community, is determined by social work colleagues. Liaison with practitioner services can then take place, as appropriate, for updating and transfer of medical casenotes. Our model suggests that units liaise early with the allied GP surgeries to clarify registration status, highlighting this clearly in unit records and avoiding subsequent confusion about which GP to contact.

HEALTH ASSESSMENT

The previous into care medicals presented problems to all parties involved. In particular, GPs were often left at short notice, without casenotes, to assess a frightened young person without parental input and whose carer had little or no background health information to hand.

We have organised to withdraw the need for GPs to perform into care medicals. Initial health assessments, actioned through the nurse for looked after children with the support of the community paediatric teams, has resulted in highlighting areas likely to be of concern to primary health care teams. There may be a need for targeted health interventions, most appropriately dealt with by or through the GP surgery such as 'catch up' health promotion and prevention including immunisation. This will be highlighted by the initial health assessment and shared with the primary health care team.

The local GP surgery will still attend to the immediate health needs of individual young people as they become resident, if required.

CASENOTES AND CONTINUITY

For good reasons, full casenotes are only transferred to the new GP surgery when a patient fully registers. Casenotes are seen as crucial in primary care to maintain continuity of care and a record of interventions, referrals and preventive care. They are used as a resource by all members of the primary healthcare team both for individual consultations and planning and for practice-wide audit. In the past, these casenotes and the resulting continuity have broken down for looked after and accommodated young people. A series of temporary GP surgeries has resulted in the production of a disparate record without central collation.

Negotiations with our local Practitioner Services Division (PSD) about specific collation of the GP casenotes for these young people has resulted in agreement that these records may be 'fast-tracked' to practices on request. To enhance this record, our model proposes that a copy of the health record produced by the nurse for looked after children is transferred from the LAC system to the GP casenotes, either centrally via PSD or directly to the practice.

HEALTH PROMOTION

The maintenance of a health agenda in residential units has been challenging. We have recognised the need to aid those who care for the children and young people in their role of health care monitoring.

The training which we have worked hard on with our local social work departments, and on a national basis with the Scottish Institute for Residential Child Care, has been significant in helping to support care workers. Perhaps, more importantly, the presence of our project nurses helped secure a focus for health in the activity of residential units. In discussion at PCT and LHCC level, there was strong recognition of the public health nursing element of this work.

The allied primary health care team model proposes a role for a named nurse to liaise more closely from within the practice with the local residential unit in order to maintain the health agenda. This might be a health visitor or practice nurse. Through an improved understanding of ways of working, the named nurse aims to foster better links between primary care practitioners and carers, encouraging more reflective approaches by care workers.

Allied to this development, the nurse for LAC is developing a local support structure for nurses with a particular interest in improving the health outcomes for looked after children. On a national level, the RCHP nurses have inaugurated a nurse special interest group in this area (see Part 3, page 89) and it is apparent that nurses working with looked after children nationwide are from backgrounds of community child health, school nursing and primary care.

COMMUNITY DENTAL SERVICE

As part of the primary care strategy, work has been ongoing to *enhance links with the community dental service*. Each unit now has an effective working relationship with the local community dental service, so that a service is in place for each home to use when young people have no dentist. Advocacy work with the community dental staff explained the special needs of this group of young people, and the service is proving very helpful. With the earlier assessment of needs of young people entering the care system, workers are being encouraged to take the young people for dental care at an earlier stage (see Part 5, page 87).

COMMUNITY PHARMACY SERVICE

At the health training week for carers organised by RCHP, the *role of the community pharmacy* was emphasised as an excellent potential support for carers in dealing with day-to-day minor ailments. Carers were encouraged to seek advice from their local pharmacist, and work continues involving the development of guidelines for carers regarding the use and storage of medications within units.

Strategy within social work

The RCHP was set up to look innovatively at an area of health care and health service delivery which was not proving effective in its existing form. It has provided an opportunity to look at roles and responsibilities not only within health, but also within social work through a concerted effort to liaise closely with our local departments.

For improvements to be effective and lasting, it was necessary to bring about a change in practice at all levels, from those directly involved with young people to those who make the policies affecting their health. Consultation has taken place in partnership with social work practitioners, as well as with social work management, regarding new ways of working.

Because we have been operating in another agency's workplace, it would be impossible to effect permanent change without this being developed as departmental policy by social work management, and we have been very fortunate in the support afforded by the local social work departments.

There have been several occasions where social work has funded or co-funded initiatives within the project (for example, the launch, training, health resource pack and end of project conference) which is, in itself, acknowledgement that improving the health care for the looked after and accommodated young people is a shared responsibility.

Implementing the new way of working, to take ownership of health from the time of entry into the care system, has necessitated *radical changes in social work working policy,* achieved through close interagency collaboration. Mutual trust and understanding has proved invaluable. An evaluation of the new system, through consultation with social workers and carers, both residential and foster, has demonstrated a high degree of satisfaction with the new method of working.

Other main areas of change for social work include developments in *staff training* (see Part 5, page 84), the evolving role of the residential care *health link worker* and the *unit held health record* (see Part 5, page 82). The *health resource pack* (see Part 3, page 71) will provide support for residential care practitioners in the longer term. An *Interagency Residential Care Health Steering Group* has been set up to continue the work of the project steering group at the end of the RCHP.

Foremost among the developments which we have seen is the firm establishment of health and education, as equally responsible partners, with social work in caring for the children and young people in the care system.

Part 5 Summary of principal themes and key recommendations

The Residential Care Health Project has worked in partnership with social services to examine and develop the entire health care system for children and young people looked after and accommodated by the local authority in residential care in Edinburgh, East Lothian and Midlothian (the area covered by Lothian University NHS Trust). This has been achieved through a team approach, based on a nursing infrastructure, involving professionals drawn from several different backgrounds of healthcare including community child health, primary care (general practice and health visiting), school nursing and mental health, with clerical support.

The emphasis has been on the identification and assessment of key areas of concern, and on moving to sustainable change. This, in turn, has developed to encompass the needs of children who are looked after and accommodated in foster care as well as in residential care.

The following summarises the principal themes in the different areas of work, and lists the key recommendations for sustainable improvement in the health care of children and young people looked after and accommodated in residential care.

Health assessment of the children and young people

- Comprehensive health assessments were carried out on 105 children and young people
- Average age was 13.9 (ranges 6.3-17.8: median 14 years)

PRINCIPAL THEMES

- The majority were not on a mainstream school roll
- The study uncovered a large number of physical health needs which were not previously recognised
- Many conditions had been known about in the past, but had been lost to follow-up
- Over a quarter had disorders of motor development, and almost one in five had learning difficulties
- 97% had emotional, behavioural or mental health problems
- 71% had incomplete immunisations
- More than half required dental care
- Direct access to health records prior to assessment could identify much of the missed health care
- There were high levels of risk-taking activity

KEY RECOMMENDATIONS

- Each child requires a comprehensive assessment of their health as soon as practicable after the point of entry into the care system
- This assessment should be aimed at rectifying omissions in health care and promoting the future better health of the child
- A meaningful assessment must be preceded by the collation of background health information on the child
- The assessment must include that of the child's development, mental health and health promotion needs
- It must be proactive and inform the health care plan for the child, with support to access required services to rectify gaps in health care

- It is likely that the vast majority of young people in residential care will not access a complete health education programme at school, and carers need to be aware of this
- The high level of developmental and learning difficulties highlights the need for dedicated educational assessments and supports for looked after children
- There is a pressing need to develop and prioritise mental health services for looked after children
- Promoting healthier lifestyles is a very important aspect of a child's placement
- A clear confidentiality statement is needed, in agreement with social work colleagues

Health information and records at unit level

One of the greatest difficulties in managing the health care of looked after and accommodated children is the organisation and tracking of their health information. At the outset of the RCHP, therefore, an audit was carried out of the quality and comprehensiveness of health information held at unit level in the health section of the files of the young people. The key areas analysed reflected those required by the Scottish Executive 'Looking After Children' materials. The results were used to underpin development and change in the recording and storing of health information in partnership with social work colleagues.

PRINCIPAL THEMES

- More than half of the children had no written health assessment at unit level
- Where information was forthcoming, there was a huge discrepancy between that held by the units and the true health profile of the population, as seen by the results from the health assessments of the young people in the RCHP
- The health records held at unit level were not a useful source of information about the children and young people, and could not reliably inform carers on meeting the child's health needs
- The health records would not be a reliable source of background health information for health professionals attending to the children

KEY RECOMMENDATIONS

The previous system of a single Reception into Care (RIC) medical was clearly not effective in ensuring that sufficient health information is available for carers. It concentrates on the state of health of the child at the time of entry into the care system, and does not address the issues of early neglect, missed health care, health promotional needs, development, mental health and emotional wellbeing. This information is necessary to ensure that the experience of being looked after and accommodated can be as nurturing and therapeutic as possible for the child or young person.

- Looked after children must have access to health care, screening and preventive services which equal that of those not in the care system
- Any omissions in health care provision must be identified when the child becomes accommodated, and carers informed so that they can be rectified
- To ensure this, all children need to have written documentation of any health issues around the time of entry into the care system, including collation of past medical history and missed health care
- Such information is based in many different health systems (primary care, community child health, hospital records, health IT systems, etc.)
- Collating this type of health information would be impossible to achieve without input from a dedicated health professional to access these systems

- Health assessments need to identify action required to improve the current health of the child, with this entered in care plans
- Assessment of educational needs is an essential part of the holistic assessment of the child
- Unit held health records must keep *all health information together* in an easily accessed format
- They need to be *easily available* for carers, or for any health professional attending the young person
- Health records need to move *with the young person* when placements change ensuring that vital health information is not missing on arrival at a new placement

The primary care of looked after children and young people in residential care

Access to health services in the UK is primarily through registration with a local general practitioner. For looked after children, this depends fundamentally on the relationship of the young person with their carers, and, subsequently, on the relationships and structures existing between residential units and local GP surgeries. Two primary care needs assessments were carried out to understand better these latter relationships.

PRINCIPAL THEMES
- Within units, care staff find it difficult to clarify health problems, particularly mental health problems, and may be uncertain whom to approach for help
- Some care staff tend to be reactive in their approach, choosing to respond to health needs seen to be 'immediate' rather than being proactive and choosing to plan ahead for longer-term health needs
- Care staff feel that some GPs and surgery staff do not understand the nature of their work and the predicament of looked after children
- Young people can miss out on the benefits of full registration at a local GP surgery, ending up with incomplete casenotes and missed preventive care, with chronic problems lost to follow-up

KEY RECOMMENDATIONS
- Closer working links between residential care staff and staff at the local GP surgery, in particular, links between the health link worker on the unit and the practice manager and an appropriate nurse at the allied GP surgery
- Clarification of the appropriate GP at the time of placement
- Full registration of young people with the allied GP surgery by 12 weeks into placement
- Closer working links between allied GP surgeries and Practitioner Services Division (PSD) for the central collation and fast tracking of GP notes
- Closer working links between allied GP surgeries and community child health departments, in particular with the nurse for looked after children
- Action in response to the recommendations of the initial LAC health assessment, through liaison between the nurse for looked after children and the allied GP surgery

Residential care staff training and development

Looking after children and young people away from their homes and families puts a very high burden of responsibility on those who care, particularly when dealing with health issues. An audit was carried out on the needs and wishes of staff for health training, by means of a staff questionnaire. Out of 322 which were delivered, 186 (57.8%) were returned. The average length of employment within residential child care of the responders was nine years (ranges three months to 30 years).

PRINCIPAL THEMES

- Significant numbers of staff said they had little or no training on a range of health topics
- Further training was requested on a wide range of health issues
- Training in health issues was welcomed at all levels from foundation to experienced practitioner level
- Collaboration between social work and health provided an excellent basis for sustainable health training

KEY RECOMMENDATIONS

- Health and social work need to work together to ensure adequate training of staff in health issues
- This training should be an essential part of residential care practitioner training
- The setting up of a network of health link workers in units is helpful in identifying a target group for higher training who can work in units to implement change and development
- A period as a health link worker should be an essential part of higher professional development for residential care practitioners
- There is a need to develop health training and resources for practitioners at a national level

PROMOTING BETTER HEALTH

The RCHP has taken a holistic view of health promotion throughout, and has developed the concept of the health promoting unit. The activities of the project have been largely concerned with health education, health promotion and training in a wide range of health issues, particularly aimed at carers.

PRINCIPAL THEMES

- The young people may be very wary of strangers wanting to work with them on health promotional issues
- Their carers are the people to whom they are most likely to go to for support
- Carers have a crucial role within the home in the promotion of better health for the children in their care
- Carers need to be well informed about a wide range of health issues and to be aware of all available sources of support for the young people, and for themselves
- Many looked after and accommodated children miss out on school-based health promotion and health education programmes
- There is a need for a comprehensive health resource pack for carers to help them identify further sources of advice and support on health issues

As well as encouraging units to integrate healthy lifestyles into their day-to-day living, certain areas of children's and young peoples' health require particular attention regarding health promotion and health education.

These include:

- Mental health
- Sexual health
- Drug, alcohol and/or volatile substance abuse
- Dental health
- Immunisation uptake
- Promoting better health within secure units

Mental health issues were consistently identified from the start of the project as the single most pressing area in which residential care staff felt the need for support in helping young people within units. A mental health practitioner was appointed within the project, to look at key areas of concern, and to make recommendations as to the most effective supports for young people and their carers. The findings from the study of health profiles of the young people, and the results of the staff training audit also made specific comment about mental health issues.

Promoting better health

MENTAL HEALTH

PRINCIPAL THEMES: UNDERLYING PROBLEMS

- Very high rates of emotional, behavioural and mental health problems (health assessment profiles of children and young people)
- Difficulty in engaging young people, especially when seen by an unfamiliar adult
- Young people are often unwilling to attend specialist mental health services
- Units can be frightening, with young people experiencing high levels of anxiety
- Carers feel unsupported and inadequately trained to deal with the very extreme problems that these young people present
- Staffing problems and changes in carers and social workers can be detrimental to emotional security
- Admission policies can cause huge disruptions among previously stable groups of young people
- Mental health services can be reluctant to become involved because of 'unstable care situations'
- Mental health is viewed very differently by residential care and mental health practitioners
- Carers can have unrealistic expectations of what child and adolescent mental health services have to offer

PRINCIPAL THEMES: WORK WITH STAFF AND YOUNG PEOPLE

- Help tends to be sought later rather than sooner
- High levels of psychosocial impairment may mask huge levels of anxiety and distress
- Staff have great faith in interventions but young people might not be interested in engaging
- Inconsistencies in management between workers underlie many management difficulties
- Different criteria for intervention: need for uniformity for all staff
- Staff often feel powerless, threatened, bullied and harassed by children and young people
- Contact with parents often brings traumas, disappointments and frustration to young people
- Need to look at key 'flashpoints' for behaviour
- Need to learn to listen rather than to react

KEY RECOMMENDATIONS

- Residential care staff need prompt and easy access to consultation and support on a wide range of emotional, behavioural and mental health problems
- Training in mental health issues is a vital part of residential care practitioner employee development
- Training must focus less on crisis intervention, and more on the underlying root causes of mental and emotional ill health
- There is a need to help other health professionals understand the very real problems of unit staff working with very troubled young people
- The emotional, behavioural and mental health problems of looked after and accommodated young people cannot be looked at in isolation from their life experiences
- The needs of this group of young people, and of those who care for them, are very specific. As such, there is a need for child and adolescent mental health services (CAMHS) to develop dedicated practitioners or teams with an expertise in managing the mental health needs of looked after children

Sexual health

The RCHP set out to help young people achieve better standards of sexual health, and to be more in control of the choices they make regarding sexual activity and the risk of unwanted pregnancy. Good sexual health was placed in the domain of a healthy lifestyle, and there has been an acknowledgement of the role of carers in guiding and supporting young people appropriately in the absence of family support and role models.

PRINCIPAL THEMES

- Young people in local authority residential care are unlikely to be able to reliably access the standard school health education curriculum
- Those who care for young people need to be able to advise and support young people, and to be aware of available services
- As such, carers need access to appropriate training and advice on sexual health issues
- Improving sexual health goes much wider than merely addressing issues directly related to sexual health
- Factors which adversely affect sexual health for any population (including low self esteem, mental health problems, poor educational outcomes and goals, drug, alcohol and volatile substance abuse) are very prevalent in this group, and are likely to impede any attempt to improve sexual health unless they too are robustly addressed
- Delivering sexual health promotion to hard-to-reach, marginalised young people takes time and effort
- For outside specialist agencies to deliver health promotion advice to young people in residential care effectively, it is most effective to work in partnership with agencies (health, education and social work) already involved with young people in residential care
- The experience of working in partnership with Healthy Respect was an effective way of ensuring access to services and enabling specialist services to access the young people and care staff

KEY RECOMMENDATIONS

- Sexual health needs to be looked at in the context of holistic health improvement
- Policy and practice must be developed with the specific needs of this group of young people in mind, and must be included in the regional sexual health strategy
- Young people who do not trust adults need to be supported by those whom they do trust
- Carers need to be supported by health agencies to be able to advise young people on sexual health matters, with access to good training programmes
- Better links with education services and school nurses will help to ensure that the gaps in the school health education programme are covered for young people who cannot access the standard curriculum
- Within specialist sexual health promotion agencies, there is a need for dedicated services for vulnerable young people, particularly those who are looked after and accommodated

Drug, alcohol and volatile substance abuse

The RCHP prioritised addressing the needs of young people in residential care regarding access to drug and alcohol advisory services. The geographical area, served by the RCHP, was fortunate in having some excellent initiatives for young people under way at the outset regarding drug, alcohol and volatile substance use, both in terms of education for young people and carers, and individual counselling and support for young people.

The role of the RCHP was therefore to liaise closely with these services, and to encourage and facilitate the uptake of services by young people and staff.

PRINCIPAL THEMES

- High rates of drug and alcohol use among the young people (comprehensive health assessments)
- Training in drugs, alcohol and volatile substance abuse was identified as a priority training need in the RCHP staff training audit
- Poor school attendance results in missed health education at school
- Availability of easy access support for young people is invaluable
- Carers, health and education professionals also have prompt access to advice
- Good interagency working results in clarity of planning to support young people

KEY RECOMMENDATIONS

- A multi-agency approach is needed to ensure support for young people regarding drug, alcohol and volatile substance misuse
- There is a need for education services for young people, and also for counselling and support for young misusers
- There is a need to target young people who are looked after and accommodated as they miss out on the health education curriculum at school due to poor attendance
- Residential care practitioners require ongoing training on the recognition of drug and alcohol abuse, and on how to support young people who are affected

Dental health

Lothian Oral Health Strategy priority targets include all children in areas of deprivation and their parents and carers. Recommendations include healthy eating guidelines, a multi-agency approach to promoting oral health, and working with Community Dental Services to promote dental care in areas of poor uptake.

The RCHP therefore worked with the local community dental services to raise the profile of oral health from the outset, culminating in a dental health awareness initiative during National Smile Week in May 2002.

PRINCIPAL THEMES

- High level of need for dental assessment and oral health promotion identified at health assessments
- Working with local community dentists was invaluable for those children who did not have established links with a dentist
- Oral health can be incorporated into a holistic view of health promotion and health care for children and young people
- With commitment from carers, better oral health habits can be encouraged
- With commitment from carers, good dental attendance can be achieved

KEY RECOMMENDATIONS

- There is a need to raise awareness of oral health and dental care within residential care settings
- Linking with the community dental service is an effective way to provide dental care for children who do not have an established link with an identified dentist
- Oral health needs to be viewed in the context of holistic health care
- Oral health and dental care needs to be addressed in health training for residential care practitioners

Immunisations

PRINCIPAL THEMES

- Out of the children and young people seen by the RCHP paediatrician, 71% had incomplete courses of immunisation
- Improving immunisation uptake was a key priority

KEY RECOMMENDATIONS

- The immunisation status of all children must be ascertained on becoming looked after and accommodated
- Immunisation courses should be updated as soon as possible after becoming accommodated
- Immunisation services need to be flexible to accommodate the needs of hard to reach groups of children
- Carers need to be trained on immunisation as a part of holistic health-care training

Secure units

Secure accommodation is a small but necessary part of the network of services for children. Those placed in secure units have been found to be a significant danger to themselves or to others in the community. There are many regulations around the welfare, quality of care, and rights of children in secure accommodation. The RCHP has been moving towards a gold standard of integrated health care for Edinburgh's secure units and, as such, has worked with community child health, primary care, social services, mental health and education services to develop a care package for the young people.

KEY THEMES AND RECOMMENDATIONS

- A full and comprehensive interagency assessment of the needs of the young person is invaluable
- There is a need for close working between primary care, community child health and the secure unit to assist care planning
- There is a requirement for established health protocol between secure units, primary care and community child health
- There is a training requirement in secure units for the management of extreme risk-taking behaviour, addiction and mental health disturbance
- There is a need for flexible arrangements for access to primary care services
- It is invaluable to link with a primary care practice sympathetic to the unique needs of young people in secure units and those who care for them
- There is a requirement for mutual understanding of work practice between secure units and allied GP practice
- Accessing services in the wider community – for example, hospital services and specialist services – can be problematic
- The period in secure care is one where the child is safe, with reduced levels of adverse environmental distraction, when therapeutic work may be undertaken
- There is a need for access to a full range of mental health support including forensic psychiatry

KEY RECURRING THEMES AND RECOMMENDATIONS FOR SUSTAINABILITY

- No one agency alone can improve the health outcomes for looked after children
- Recognition is needed by health agencies of the effects of frequent care moves and loss of continuity on health care
- Looked after children do not fit well into our health systems, which are set up for children who remain within their own communities and schools: flexibility of approach is required
- Central ownership of the process needs to be adopted by health agencies instead of expecting social services to manoeuvre their way around unfamiliar systems
- A nursing infrastructure similar to that of health visitors for the under fives is ideally suited to addressing the unmet health needs of those young people and identifying appropriate sources of support
- Support and training for carers, whether for residential care practitioners or foster carers, is essential for sustainable improvement
- A responsive, effective service requires dedication at all levels within social work, health, education and all working within the care system to bring about radical changes and developments in service delivery.

Conclusion

The Residential Care Health Project has addressed one particular area of child health provision, that of caring for the health of children and young people in residential care. The lessons we have learned, however, go much wider. The problems around delivery of good health packages to excluded and hard to reach young people are very complex, and involve the entire fabric of health service delivery. As such, the problems cannot be solved overnight. However, we feel that we have had a valuable opportunity to examine and realign services to the benefit of our young people, along with the chance to support carers in their 'parental' role. In so doing, we hope that we have helped the various agencies to adapt and develop an element of flexibility and innovation, bringing about a truly integrated approach to ensure universal access for all children to all health services.

Further Reading

The Abilities of Babies. Griffiths R. University of London Press. 1954.

The Abilities of Young Children. Griffiths R. ARICD. 1971.

The Biology of the Autistic Syndromes. Gillberg C, Coleman M. Mac Keith Press. 2000.

Adoption: A New Approach. Cm 5017. Department of Health White Paper. The Stationery Office. 2000.

Age of Legal Capacity (Scotland) Act 1991. HMSO. 1991.

Assessment of the Drug Education Needs of Vulnerable Young People in Edinburgh. Fast Forward Positive Lifestyles. 2001.

Care Sick: The Physical and Mental Health Needs of a Sample of Young People in Local Authority and Residential Care. Robinson P, Auckland K, Crawford H, Nevison C. Young People's Unit, Royal Edinburgh Hospital. 1999.

Child Care Law: Scotland: A Summary. Plumtree A. British Agencies for Adoption & Fostering. 1997.

Children Looked After by Local Authorities. (Second Report). House of Commons Select Committee on Health. The Stationery Office. 1998.

Children (Scotland) Act 1995. The Stationery Office. 1995.

Children (Scotland) Act 1995: Regulations and Guidance. Social Work Services Group, Scottish Office. The Scottish Office. 1997.

Conners' Rating Scale Revised 1997. Conners CK. MHS. 1997.

Criminal Procedure (Scotland) Act 1995. The Stationery Office. 1995.

A Drugs Strategy for the City of Edinburgh 1999-2000. City of Edinburgh Council, Lothian Health, Lothian and Borders Police, Coalition of Drug Agencies, HM Prison Edinburgh. City of Edinburgh Council. 1999.

For Scotland's Children. Scottish Executive. 2001.

Health Empowerment Project. Sinclair L. Lothian Primary Care Trust. 2000. (Unpublished).

The Health Needs of Young People Leaving Care. Saunders L, Broad B. Leicester: De Montfort University, Department of Social and Community Studies. 1997.

The Health Promoting School: Focusing on Health and School Improvement. Boddington N, Hull T. Forbes Publications. 1996.

Health Record. British Agencies for Adoption & Fostering. Undated.

Learning with Care: The Education of Children Looked After Away from Home by Local Authorities. HM Inspectors of Schools, Social Work Services Inspectorate. The Stationery Office. 2001.

Let's Talk About Sex and Relationships: Developing and Reviewing Policy. Pate-Kanwal H, Lenderyou GF. National Children's Bureau. 1998.

Lothian Local Health Plan 2002. Lothian Health Board. 2002.

Lothian Oral Health Strategy. Lothian Health Board. 1998.

Maclure Reading Type for Children. Clarke C. HS International. Undated.

National Care Standards: Care Homes for Children and Young People. National Care Standards Committee. Scottish Executive. 2002.

Oral Health Strategy for Scotland. The Scottish Office. 1995.

Psychological Problems in Young People 'Accommodated' by Glasgow City Council. Chetwynd P, Robb L. Greater Glasgow Primary Healthcare NHS Trust. 1999.

Quick Neurological Screening Test (2nd ed. rev.). Mutti M, Sterling H, Spalding N. Academic Therapy Publications. 1998.

Remember My Messages. Shaw C. The Who Cares? Trust. 1998.

Report of the 1998/99 Scottish Health Board's Dental Epidemiological Programme Survey of 14 Year Old Children. Pitts NB, Nugent ZJ, Smith PA. University of Dundee Dental Health Services Research Unit. 1999.

Report of the Programme Team for Health Needs of Young People in Residential Care 1992-1997. Nottingham Community Health NHS Trust. The University of Nottingham. 1998.

The Scientific Basis of Dental Health Education: A Policy Document. (Rev 4th ed.) Health Development Agency. 2001.

Scotland's Health: A Challenge to Us All: A Policy Statement. The Scottish Office. HMSO. 1992.

A Study of the Contact of Children in Residential Care with Mental Health Services. Perry M. University of Edinburgh Special Studies Module. Unpublished paper. 2001.

Tackling Drugs in Scotland: Action in Partnership. The Scottish Office. 1999.

Tackling Drugs to Build a Better Britain: The Government's Ten-Year Strategy for Tackling Drugs Misuse. Cm 3945. The Stationery Office. 1998.

Towards A Healthier Scotland: A White Paper on Health. The Scottish Office. The Stationery Office. 1999.

Working Together for a Healthier Scotland. The Scottish Office. The Stationery Office. 1998.

Journal Articles

Better Health for Children in Residential Care. Polnay L, Glaser A, Rao V. *Arch Dis Child.* Sep 1996; 75: 263-265.

Catching Children as They Fall: Mental Health Promotion in Residential Child Care in East Dunbartonshire. Van Beinum M, Martin A, Bonnet C. *Scottish Journal of Residential Child Care.* Aug 2002; 1 (1): 14-22.

Continuity and Discontinuity of Attachment from Infancy through Adolescence. Hamilton CE. *Child Development.* May/June 2000; 71 (3): 690-694.

Correlates of Therapy Referral in Foster Children. Cantos AL, Gries LT, Slis V. *Child Abuse & Neglect.* October 1996; 20 (10): 921-931.

Cross Sectional Survey of Meningococcal C Immunisation in Children Looked After by Local Authorities and Those Living at Home. Hill CM, Mather M, Goddard J. *BMJ.* Feb 2003; 326: 364-365.

Depression, Parenthood, and Age at First Birth. Mirowsky J, Ross CE. *Soc Sci Med.* Apr 2002; 54 (8): 1281-1289.

Development of a Short Questionnaire for Use in Epidemiological Studies of Depression in Children and Adolescents. Angold A, Costello EJ, Messer SC, Pickles A, Winder F, Silver D. *International Journal of Methods in Psychiatric Research.* Dec 1995; 5 (4): 237-249.

Drinking, Smoking and Illicit Drug Use Among 15 and 16 Year Olds in the United Kingdom. Miller PM, Plant M. *BMJ.* Aug 1996; 313: 394-397.

Early Life and Later Determinants of Adult Disease: A 50 Year Follow-up Study of the Newcastle Thousand Families Cohort. Lamont DW, Parker L, Cohen MA, White M, Bennet SMA, Unwin NC, Craft AW, Alberti KG. *Public Health.* 1998; 112 (2): 85-93.

The European Network of Health Promoting Schools: An Alliance of Health, Education and Democracy. Rasmussen VB, Rivett D. *Health Education.* Mar 2000; 100 (2): 61-67.

Health Knowledge and Health Education in the Democratic Health-Promoting School. Jensen BB. *Health Education.* Jul/Aug 2000; 100 (4): 146-153.

Health of Socially Excluded Groups: Lessons Must Be Applied. Grant AM. *BMJ.* Nov 2001; 323: 1071.

Health of Teenagers in Residential Care: Comparison of Data Held by Care Staff with Data in Community Child Health Records. Bundle A. *Arch Dis Child.* Jan 2001; 84: 10-14.

Health Promotion and Public Health: A Model in Action. Tannahill A. *Community Medicine.* Feb 1998; 10 (1): 48-51.

He's Leaving Home. George M. *Community Care.* Jun/Jul 1997; 1178: 29-30.

A History of Abuse and Negative Life Events in Patients with a Sexually Transmitted Disease and in a Community Sample. Pitzner JK, McGarry-Long J, Drummond PD. *Child Abuse & Neglect.* May 2000; 24 (5): 715-731.

Inspection of Care Arrangements and Education in: Secure Units Howdenhall and St Katharine's Centres. City of Edinburgh Council: Joint Report by Social Work Services Inspectorate and HM Inspectorate of Education. Scottish Executive. December 2001.

Improving Teenagers' Knowledge of Emergency Contraception: Cluster Randomised Controlled Trial of a Teacher Led Intervention. Graham A, Moore L, Sharp D, Diamond I. *BMJ.* May 2002; 324: 1179.

Improving the Health Care Process and Determining Health Outcomes of Children Looked After by the Local Authority. Payne H, Butler I. *Ambulatory Child Health.* 1998; 4: 165-172.

Interventions to Reduce Unintended Pregnancies Among Adolescents: Systematic Review of Randomised Controlled Trials. DiCenso A, Guyatt G, Willan A, Griffith L. *BMJ.* Jun 2002; 324: 1426.

Limits of Teacher Delivered Sex Education: Interim Behavioural Outcomes from Randomised Trial. Wight D, Raab GM, Henderson M, Abraham C, Buston K, Hart G, Scott S. *BMJ.* Jun 2002 : 1430.

Looking After Health: A Joint Working Approach to Improving the Health Outcomes of Looked After and Accommodated Children and Young People. Grant AM, Ennis J, Stuart F. *Scottish Journal of Residential Child Care.* Aug 2002; 1 (1): 23-29.

Mental Health of Children in Foster Care: A Comparison with Community and Clinical Samples. Stein E. Canadian *Journal of Psychiatry.* Aug 1996; 41 (6); 385-391.

Neurological Soft Signs in Mainstream Pupils. Fellick JM, Thomson A, Sills J, Hart CA, Stephenson Prof JBP. *Arch Dis Child.* Nov 2001; 85: 371-374.

Prevalence of Psychiatric Disorders in Young People in the Care System. McCann JB, James A, Wilson S, Dunn G. *BMJ.* Dec 1996: 313; 1529-1530.

Psychiatric Disorder Among Children at the Time of Entering Local Authority Care: Questionnaire Survey. Dimigen G, Del Priore C, Butler S, Evans S, Ferguson L, Swan M. *BMJ.* Sept 1999; 319: 675.

Reaching All Children. Lynch MA, Gough D. *BMJ.* July 2001; 323:176-177.

Relationship of Childhood Abuse and Household Dysfunction to Many of the Leading Causes of Death in Adults: The Adverse Childhood Experiences (ACE) Study. Felitti VJ, Anda RF, Nordenberg D, Williamson DF, Spitz AM, Edwards V, Koss MP, Marks JS. *Am J Prev Med.* May 1998; 14 (4): 245-258.

The Scottish Green Paper. Commentary. Beyond a Healthy Mind in a Healthy Body. Tannahill A. *J Public Health Med.* Sep 1998; 20 (3): 249-252.

Semi-sensory Integrative Processing in Delinquent and Non-delinquent Prone Adolescents. Fanchiang A. *American Journal of Occupational Therapy.* July 1999; 44 (7): 631-638.

The Statutory Medical and Health Needs of Looked After Children: Time for a Radical Review? Mather M, Humphrey J, Robson J. *Adoption & Fostering.* Summer 1997; 21 (2): 36-40.

Success and Failure in Gonorrhoea Control. Low N, Fitzgerald MR. *Dermatol Clin.* Oct 1998; 16 (4): 713-722.

Teenage Childbearing and Long-Term Socioeconomic Consequences: A Case Study in Sweden. Olausson PO, Haglund B, Weitoft GR, Cnattingius S. *Fam Plann Perspect.* Mar/Apr 2001; 33 (2): 70.

Teenage Fertility and Life Chances. Wellings K, Wadsworth J, Johnson A, Field J, Macdowall W. *Reprod.* Sep 1999; 4 (3): 184-190.

Types of Maltreatment as a Predictor of Mental Health Service Use for Children in Foster Care. Garland AF, Landsverk JL, Hough RL, Ellis-MacLeod E. *Child Abuse & Neglect.* Aug 1996; 20 (8): 647-790.

What is Health Promotion? Tannahill A. *Health Educ J.* 1985; 44 (4): 167-168.

Some Useful Contacts

HYPE (Help for Young People in Edinburgh), Simpson House, 52 Queen Street, Edinburgh EH2 3NS. 0131-466 4600. schype@mail.nch.org.uk

Fast Forward Positive Lifestyles Ltd. 4 Bernard Street, Edinburgh EH6 6PP. 0131-554 4300. www.fastforward.org.uk

MELD (Mid and East Lothian Drugs), 4c Newmills Road, Dalkeith, Midlothian EH22 1DU. 0131-660 3566. www.meld-drugs.co.uk

Scottish Institute for Residential Child Care, University of Strathclyde, Jordanhill Campus, 76 Southbrae Drive, Glasgow G13 1PP

Index

Astron B25224 1/04